Essential Biology

Molecular Biology
&
Genetics

3rd edition

STERLING
Education

Customer Satisfaction Guarantee

Your feedback is important because we strive to provide the highest quality educational materials. Email us comments or suggestions.

info@sterling–prep.com

We reply to emails – check your spam folder

3   2   1

ISBN-13: 979-8-8855717-5-3

Sterling Education materials are available at quantity discounts.

Contact info@sterling–prep.com

Sterling Education
6 Liberty Square #11
Boston, MA 02109

© 2023 Sterling Education

Published by Sterling Education

 Printed in the U.S.A.

STERLING
Education

From the foundations of a living cell to the complex mechanisms of gene expression, *Essential Biology Self-Teaching Guides* are a comprehensive compendium of clearly explained texts to learn and master multifaceted biology topics.

These guides provide a detailed review of fundamental biological processes of living systems. Develop a better understanding of cell and molecular biology, mechanisms of cell metabolism, plants and photosynthesis, evolution and natural selection, ecology and population biology. Learn the principles of genetics, microbiology, classification and diversity, as well as structure and function of anatomical systems. Reinforce your learning by working through the practice questions and detailed explanations.

Created by highly qualified biology instructors, researchers, and education specialists, these books empower readers by helping them increase their understanding of biology.

We sincerely hope that these guides are valuable for your learning.

230720akp

Essential Biology Self-Teaching Guides

Eukaryotic Cell & Cellular Metabolism

Molecular Biology & Genetics

Nervous & Endocrine Systems

Circulatory, Respiratory & Immune Systems

Digestive & Excretory Systems

Muscle, Skeletal & Integumentary Systems

Reproduction & Development

Microbiology

Plants & Photosynthesis

Evolution, Classification & Diversity

Ecology & Population Biology

Visit our Amazon store

Essential Chemistry Self-Teaching Guides

Electronic Structure & Periodic Table

Chemical Bonding

States of Matter & Phase Equilibria

Stoichiometry

Solution Chemistry

Chemical Kinetics & Equilibrium

Acids & Bases

Chemical Thermodynamics

Electrochemistry

Visit our Amazon store

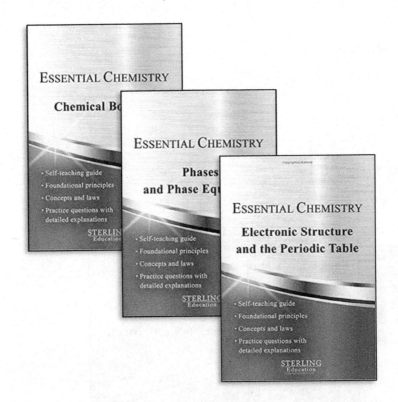

Essential Physics Self-Teaching Guides

Kinematics and Dynamics

Equilibrium and Momentum

Force, Motion, Gravitation

Work and Energy

Fluids and Solids

Waves and Periodic Motion

Light and Optics

Sound

Electrostatics and Electromagnetism

Electric Circuits

Heat and Thermodynamics

Atomic and Nuclear Structure

Visit our Amazon store

Everything You Always Wanted to Know About...

Chemistry

Physics

Cell and Molecular Biology

Organismal Biology

American History

American Law

American Government and Politics

Comparative Government and Politics

World History

European History

Psychology

Environmental Science

Human Geography

Visit our Amazon store

Page intentionally left blank

Table of Contents

Table of Contents (*continued*)

REVIEW: DNA, Protein Synthesis & Gene Expression (*continued*)

Table of Contents (*continued*)

Table of Contents (*continued*)

REVIEW: DNA, Protein Synthesis & Gene Expression (*continued*)

Table of Contents (*continued*)

Table of Contents (*continued*)

REVIEW

DNA, Protein Synthesis
&
Gene Expression

Deoxyribonucleic Acid (DNA) Structure and Function

Nucleotide composition

Deoxyribonucleic acid (DNA) is the sequence of paired nucleotides that stores the genetic code necessary for replicating and determining the sequence of amino acids in proteins.

The transcription process uses DNA as a template to form a *ribonucleic acid* (RNA), which serves as a temporary transcript of hereditary genetic information.

Ribosomes translate the information from mRNA into a sequence of amino acids to form polypeptides, folding into proteins.

DNA contains four nucleotides (adenine, cytosine, guanine, and thymine).

Nucleotides consist of 1) at least one phosphate group, 2) a pentose sugar, and 3) a one or two-ringed structure containing carbon and nitrogen (i.e., nitrogenous base). The term "base" relates to its ability to accept hydrogen ions (protons). First, glycosidic bonds link the sugar to the nitrogenous base, creating a *nucleoside* (sugar and base only), as shown below.

Nucleoside formation by a condensation reaction that joins the ribose to the adenine to form adenosine (lacking the phosphate group of a nucleotide)

Phosphodiester bonds link nucleotides between the phosphate of one nucleotide and the sugar of another

Nitrogenous base

Phosphate

Sugar

The phosphate group then links to the nucleoside similarly through a condensation reaction, forming a nucleotide (sugar, base, phosphate)

Nucleic acids assemble from nucleotides

These nucleotides form a long strand with phosphodiester bonds in the sugar-phosphate DNA backbone.

A nucleotide polymer comprises a *nucleic acid*, and its acidity is due to the phosphate groups.

Nucleic acids (i.e., RNA and DNA) store, transmit, and express genetic information in cells.

DNA has two nucleic acid strands combined to form the double-stranded DNA molecule.

Strands are joined when the bases of each strand (i.e., A = T and C ≡ G) form *base pairs*.

The DNA in a single human cell contains about 3 billion base pairs.

Because DNA has a helical twist, the coiling of the DNA strand makes the DNA compact.

The 3 billion base pairs in one human cell would stretch to about 6 feet in length.

The sequence of base pairs encodes the genetic information of the cell.

In nucleic acids, the genetic code determines the sequence of amino acids in the synthesized proteins.

Purine and pyrimidine nitrogenous bases

Early researchers knew that the genetic material must have a few necessary characteristics. It must store information used to control the development and the metabolic activities of cells, it must be stable to be accurately replicated during cell division and be transmitted for many cell cycles and between generations of offspring (i.e., progeny), and it must be able to undergo mutations, providing the genetic variability required for evolution.

The two types of nucleic acids were soon discovered: deoxyribonucleic acid (DNA) and ribonucleic acid (RNA). In the early twentieth century, researchers discovered that nucleic acids contain four types of nucleotides, the repeating units that make up the long DNA molecule.

There are four bases in DNA nucleotides. *Adenine* (A) and *guanine* (G) are purine bases and consist of two nitrogen-containing rings, while *thymine* (T) and *cytosine* (C) are pyrimidine bases and consist of one nitrogen-containing ring.

Adenine (A)
(DNA and RNA)

Guanine (G)
(DNA and RNA)

Cytosine (C)
(DNA and RNA)

Thymine (T)
(DNA only)

Uracil (U)
(RNA only)

Purines with a double ring structure

Pyrimidines with a single ring

Purines or *pyrimidines* are the two types of nucleotides within DNA.

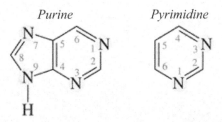

Purine   Pyrimidine

There are four different bases in DNA nucleotides. *Adenine* (A) and *guanine* (G) are purine bases and consist of two nitrogen-containing rings, while *thymine* (T) and *cytosine* (C) are pyrimidine bases and consist of only one nitrogen-containing ring.

Deoxyribose and ribose

Deoxyribose is a pentose (5-carbon) sugar in DNA.

By convention, the carbons of the sugar are numbered.

The phosphate group of DNA is attached to the 5' carbon.

Deoxyribose has a hydroxyl group (OH) at the 3' carbon (as does the ribose sugar in RNA).

Comparison of the pentose sugars in RNA (left) and DNA (right). Ribose has a 2' hydroxyl, while DNA has no oxygen (deoxy) at the 2' position

RNA has a similar but not identical structure to DNA.

The pentose sugar in RNA is *ribose*, which has the same structure as deoxyribose, except RNA has a hydroxyl group instead of hydrogen at the 2' position.

Because deoxyribose is missing this hydroxyl group, it is *deoxy* (without oxygen).

RNA contains the *uracil* pyrimidine instead of thymine (uracil replaces thymine in RNA). These two pyrimidine bases have similar structures, except for a methyl group (CH_3) present in thymine but not in uracil.

Chain elongation of DNA with the nucleophilic attack of the 5' carbon phosphate

by the 3' OH of the sugar. Elongation always proceeds 3'→5'.

By convention, the 5' phosphate end of a nucleic acid strand is written on the left,
and the 3' hydroxyl end is written on the right

Although DNA and RNA's primary structures are similar, their structures in three-dimensional space (tertiary structure) are distinct. RNA molecules are single-stranded, so base pairs can form between sections of the same molecule, resulting in shapes such as stem loops.

Double-stranded DNA is a double helix with two strands bonded in an anti-parallel orientation held by hydrogen bonds between the bases (C≡G and A=T).

Sugar-phosphate backbone of DNA

Single-stranded DNA with negatively charged sugar-phosphate backbone and bases projecting inwards when the second strand of DNA hydrogen bonds with it to form a double helix

Chargaff's rule

In the 1940s, Austrian-born biochemist Erwin Chargaff analyzed the base content of DNA using chemical techniques. Chargaff discovered that for a species, DNA has the *constancy* required of genetic material.

This constancy is *Chargaff's rule*, which states that the number of pyrimidine bases (T and C) equals the number of purine bases (A and G). The bases make hydrogen bond base pairs the same way: purine A uses a double bond with the pyrimidine T. The purine G uses a triple bond with the pyrimidine C. This is a *complementary base pairing*.

Chargaff's rule states that the number of adenines in a DNA molecule equals the number of its base pair, thymines, and the number of guanines equals the number of its base pair, cytosines. Hence, A = T and G ≡ C.

Complementary base pairing bonds A/T and G/C

Adenine has 2 hydrogen bonds to Thymine   Guanine has 3 hydrogen bonds to Cytosine

Despite the restriction of base-pair bonding, the G/C content relative to A/T content differs among species while adhering to Chargaff's rules.

Because G/C pairs have three hydrogen bonds instead of the two hydrogen bonds in A/T pairs, the strands in DNA molecules with higher G/C content are more tightly bound than those with higher A/T content.

G/C base pairs have a higher T_m (melting temperature when ½ bonds are broken) than A/T base pairs.

Although DNA has four bases (A, C, G, T) and two types of base pairs (A/T, C/G), the base sequence variability is enormous. A human chromosome contains about 140 million base pairs on average.

Since any of the four possible nucleotides are present at each nucleotide position, the number of possible nucleotide sequences in a human chromosome is $4^{140,000,000}$, or 4 raised to 140,000,000.

Use this mnemonic for which bases are purines or pyrimidines:

CUT the PIE (Cytosine, Uracil, and Thymine are pyrimidines)

PURe As Gold (purines are Adenine and Guanine)

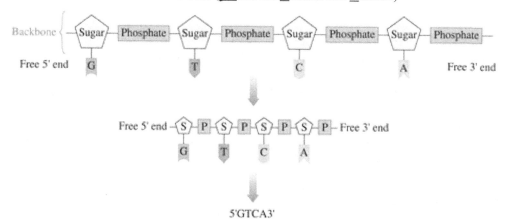

Chargaff's rule identifies the amount of all bases when one purine (A or G) and one pyrimidine (C or T) are hydrogen-bonded in a complementary-paired double-stranded DNA molecule

Watson–Crick model of DNA structure

During the 1950s, English chemist Rosalind Franklin produced X-ray diffraction photographs of DNA molecules. Rosalind Franklin's work provided evidence that DNA has a helical conformation, specifically, as two strands of DNA wind together in a double helix. A double helix can be envisioned as a twisted ladder.

American James Watson, and Englishman Francis H. C. Crick, received the Nobel Prize in 1962 for their model of DNA. Using information gathered by Chargaff and Franklin, Watson and Crick built a model of DNA in a double helix secondary structure.

Sugar-phosphate molecules form a backbone on the outside of the helix, while bases point toward the middle and form base pairs with the complementary strand. Their model was consistent with Chargaff's rules and the DNA polymer dimensions provided by Franklin's x-ray diffraction photographs of DNA.

Structure of complementary base-paired helical DNA

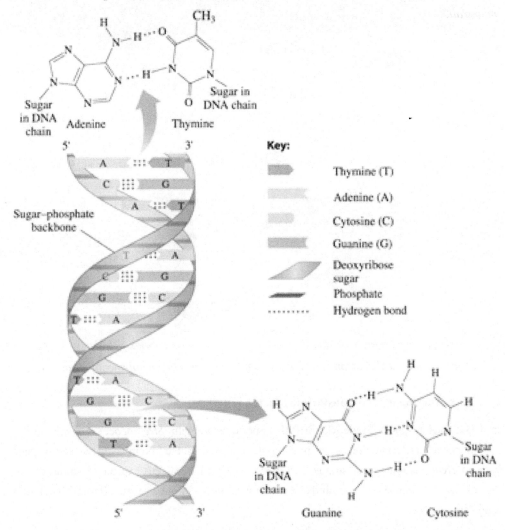

Antiparallel strands of DNA with phosphodiester bonds between the sugar-phosphate backbone.

Hydrogen bonds hold the complementary base pairs

Antiparallel strands use complementary bonding

Each strand in DNA has a direction relative to the numbering on the pentose ring. In a free nucleotide, the phosphate is attached to the 5'−phosphate of deoxyribose, while the 3'−OH of deoxyribose is exposed.

When phosphodiester bonds form, a 3' hydroxyl of one deoxyribose sugar attaches to a 5' phosphate of an incoming sugar. Thus, DNA strands have a distinct polarity, with a 5' end and a 3' end.

Two strands bound in double helix orient in opposite directions, and the two strands are *antiparallel*.

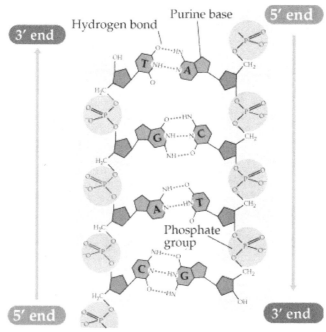

DNA as two antiparallel strands with hydrogen bonds between complementary base pairs

Griffith's experiments for transforming factor

In 1931, bacteriologist Frederick Griffith experimented with *Streptococcus pneumonia*, a pneumococcus bacterium that causes pneumonia in mammals. He first injected two sets of mice with different pneumococcus strains: a virulent strain with a mucous capsule (S strain) due to the colonies' smooth appearance and a non-virulent strain without a capsule (R strain) colonies rough appearance.

Mice injected with the S strain died, while mice injected with the R strain survived.

Griffith performed two more injections to determine if the capsule alone was responsible for the S strain's virulence. In one set of mice, he injected S strain bacteria that had been first subjected to heat ("heat-killed bacteria"). These mice survived.

In another set of mice, he injected a mixture of the heat-killed S strain and the live R strain.

These mice died, and Griffith recovered living S strain pneumococcus from the mice's bodies, despite only heat-killed S strain being injected into the live mice.

Griffith concluded that the R strain had been "transformed" by the heat-killed S strain, allowing the R strain to synthesize a capsule and become virulent.

The phenotype (virulent capsule) of the R strain bacteria must have been due to a change in genotype (genetic material), which suggested that the transforming substance must have passed from the heat-killed S strain to the R strain.

This passing of this unknown substance is *transformation*.

Avery, MacLeod, and McCarty experiment uses enzyme degradation

In 1944, molecular biologists Oswald Avery, Colin MacLeod, and Maclyn McCarty reported transforming substance in the heat-killed S strain was DNA.

This conclusion was supported by evidence showing that purified DNA resulted in transformation.

Enzymes that degrade proteins (proteases) and RNA (RNase) do not prevent a transformation.

However, using enzymes that digest DNA (DNase) does prevent transformation. Additionally, the transforming substance's molecular weight appeared great enough for genetic variability.

These results support DNA as the genetic material controlling the biosynthetic properties of a cell.

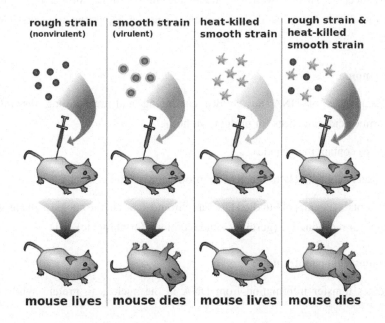

Hershey and Chase radiolabel DNA, RNA and protein

In 1952, researchers Alfred Hershey and Martha Chase performed experiments with bacteriophages (i.e., virus that infects bacteria) to confirm that DNA was the genetic material.

A *bacteriophage* (phage) is a virus that infects bacteria and consists only of a protein coat surrounding a nucleic acid core.

They used the T2 bacteriophage to infect the bacterium *Escherichia coli*, a species of intensely studied bacteria that lives within the human gut.

The purpose was to observe which bacteriophage component—the protein coat or the DNA—entered the bacterial cells and directed the reproduction of the virus.

In two experiments, they radiolabeled the bacteriophage protein coat with ^{35}S and the DNA with ^{32}P.

Each aliquot of phages infected the bacterial cells. The separate populations of bacterial progeny were lysed (blender experiment) and analyzed for the presence of isotope-labeled sulfur or phosphorus.

The progeny became labeled with ^{32}P, while the sulfur of the progeny was unlabeled, confirming that DNA (contains P), not protein (contains S), is the transmissible genetic material.

Genes and genome

Genes are sequences of DNA nucleotides containing and transmitting the information specifying amino acid sequences for protein synthesis.

DNA molecules contain many genes.

The *genome* refers collectively to the genetic information encoded in a cell.

Human cells contain 23 pairs of bundled DNA as chromosomes in the nucleus, 46 chromosomes per cell except for reproductive (germline) and red blood (erythrocyte) cells.

RNA as the messenger molecule

RNA molecules transfer information from DNA in the nucleus to protein synthesis in the cytoplasm.

RNA molecules are synthesized during transcription according to template information encoded in the hereditary molecule of DNA.

These RNA molecules are processed, and ribosomes translate mRNA to synthesize proteins.

DNA→ replication during S phase → DNA chromosome with sister chromatids

DNA → transcription → mRNA → translation → protein

DNA Replication Mechanism and Required Biomolecules

DNA replication mechanism

DNA replication is the copying of a DNA molecule. During the S (synthesis) phase of the cell cycle, DNA replicates when the strands of the double helix separate, and exposed strands act as a template for DNA synthesis.

Free deoxyribonucleoside triphosphates (dNTPs) are base-paired to form new, complementary strands.

Errors in the base sequence during replication may be corrected by a mechanism of *proofreading* DNA repair.

DNA Replication in Prokaryotes and Eukaryotes	
Prokaryotes	Eukaryotes
Five polymerases (I, II, III, IV, V)	Five polymerases $(\alpha, \beta, \gamma, \delta, \varepsilon)$
Functions of polymerase:	Functions of polymerase:
I is involved in synthesis, proofreading, repair, and removal of RNA primers	α: a polymerizing enzyme
II is also a repair enzyme	β: a repair enzyme
III is main polymerizing enzyme	γ: mitochondrial DNA synthesis
IV, V are repair enzymes under unusual conditions	δ: main polymerizing enzyme
	ε: function unknown
Polymerase are also exonucleases	Not all polymerases are exonucleases
One origin of replication	Several origins of replication
Okazaki fragments 1000-2000 residues long	Okazaki fragments 150-200 residues long
No proteins complexed to DNA	Histones complexed to DNA

This text references polymerase III and I; it substitutes the corresponding polymerases when considering eukaryotic cells. Researchers are actively investigating the exact polymerase for eukaryote's function

Replication of linear DNA in eukaryotes starts at multiple points of origin (circular DNA in prokaryotes has a single origin).

Once replication is initiated, the DNA strands separate at these points of origin as *replication bubbles*.

Replication forks

Two V-shaped separating ends of the replication bubble are sites of DNA replication or *replication forks*.

Once a strand of DNA is exposed, the enzyme *DNA polymerase III* for prokaryotes (pol γ for eukaryotes) incorporates free deoxyribonucleoside triphosphates (dNTPs) are nucleotides with three phosphate groups, into the complementary strand by catalyzing the exergonic loss of phosphate.

The two phosphate groups cleaved in the process become nucleotides and release energy (−ΔG), making the overall polymerization reaction thermodynamically favorable, thus driving the reaction forward.

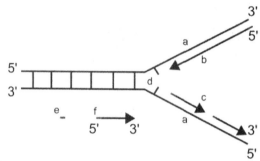

DNA replication: a: template strands, b: leading strand, c: lagging strand, d: replication fork, e: RNA primer, f: Okazaki fragment

Polymerization occurs on both strands and ends of the replication bubbles until the entire DNA is replicated, resulting in two complementary DNA molecules.

Eukaryotes replicate their DNA at a relatively slow pace of 500 to 5,000 base pairs per minute, taking hours to complete replication.

In comparison, prokaryotes can replicate their DNA faster than 500 base pairs per second.

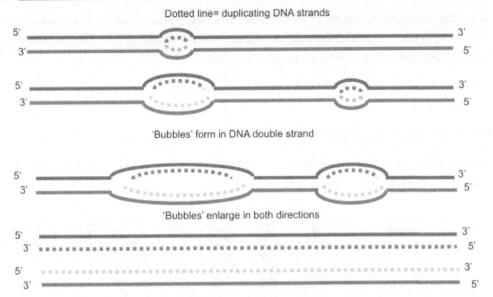

The time sequence of DNA replication process with 'bubbles' joining to form complementary DNA

Stages of DNA replication

The process of DNA replication is divided into three steps:

1. *Unwinding*—the enzyme *DNA helicase* unwinds the double helix, pulling the DNA strands apart and breaking hydrogen bonds between base pairs. Each separated strand is now a template for synthesizing a new (daughter) strand of DNA.

2. *Complementary base pairing*—free dNTPs form hydrogen bonds with their complementary base pair. Adenine pairs with thymine, and guanine pairs with cytosine.

3. *Joining*—DNA polymerase (III or γ) catalyzes nucleotides into the new strand. Incoming dNTPs cleave two phosphate groups, becoming nucleotides (one phosphate group). They are incorporated in a 5' to 3' direction, and the deoxyribose sugar and phosphate are covalently added.

DNA replication is semiconservative

In 1958, Matthew Meselson and Franklin Stahl provided evidence for the model of DNA replication. They first grew bacteria in a medium with heavy nitrogen (^{15}N) and then switched the bacteria to light nitrogen (^{14}N) for further divisions.

When they measured the density of the replicated DNA using centrifugation, they observed that the density of the replicated DNA was intermediate—less dense than a molecule made entirely with ^{15}N, but denser than a molecule made entirely with ^{14}N.

After one division, these hybrid DNA molecules (1 light and 1 heavy strand) were present in the cells.

Half the DNA molecules were light after two divisions, and half were hybrid.

These results support the *semiconservative model,* one of three main theoretical models originally proposed in DNA replication.

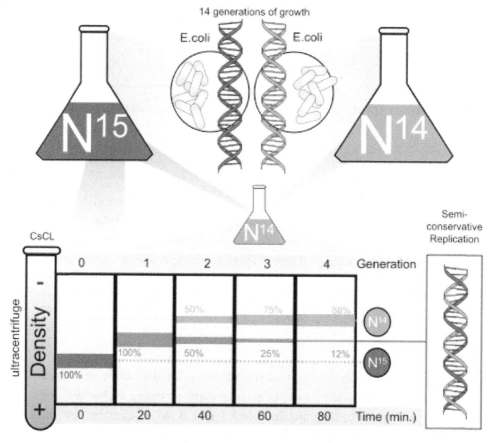

Meselson-Stahl experiment during replication with heavy nitrogen as the original growth medium

DNA replication is semiconservative because the daughter double helix consists of one parental strand and one new strand, meaning that half of the double helix is conserved from material in the parent generation.

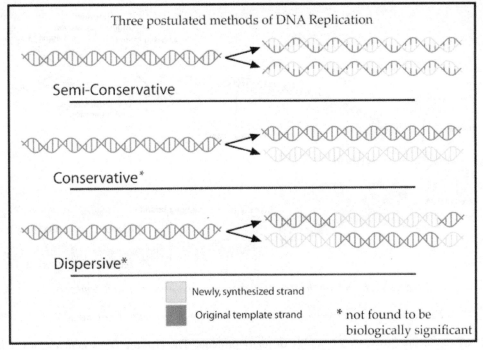

Three models of DNA replication with semi-conservative replication supported by experimentation

Three competing models for DNA replication

In a *conservative model*, one entire double strand acts as the template, while the new double strand is composed entirely *de novo* (i.e., from the beginning, new).

If this model were accurate, Meselson and Stahl's experiment would produce only heavy and light DNA molecules in the daughter cells, with no hybrid strands of intermediate density.

In a *dispersive model*, the parent double-strand is made into two new strands, with daughters containing a mixture of old and newly-incorporated nucleotides.

The two densities in the DNA of the cells in the second generation of the Meselson and Stahl experiment were inconsistent with the dispersive model.

That model would have resulted in DNA of a single density.

Specific enzymes involved in replication

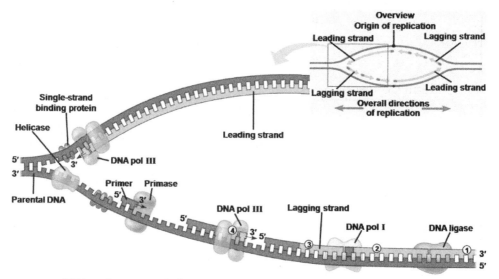

DNA replication with the associated protein involved in strand synthesis.

Pol III is used by prokaryotes and is functionally equivalent to γ in eukaryotes

DNA replication involves a complex of many proteins. The enzyme DNA *helicase* unwinds DNA to expose each template strand for DNA synthesis, forming two Y-shaped replication forks on the two sides of each replication bubble. ATP hydrolysis is required for helicase to break the hydrogen bonds between the complementary strands of DNA. *Single-stranded binding proteins* (SSBP) attach to exposed single strands to keep them from reforming base-pair hydrogen bonds, as well as to prevent degradation by DNase. *Topoisomerase* relieves tension in the DNA supercoiling and prevents knots by breaking and rejoining strands. This is essential in allowing helicase to unwind the DNA without causing tension elsewhere along the DNA strand.

DNA polymerase III in prokaryotes (γ in eukaryotes), the primary polymerase responsible for replication, cannot attach directly to an exposed single strand of DNA; it can only start polymerizing from an existing strand or, more specifically, from an existing nucleotide 3'−OH. The enzyme *primase* first creates a small sequence of complementary *RNA primer* of approximately 18–22 ribose bases. DNA polymerase begins synthesis after binding to this RNA primer. Primase can begin synthesis *de novo*, unlike DNA polymerase.

DNA polymerase III moves only from 3' to 5' along the template strand, synthesizing a new antiparallel strand; thus, the new strand is formed from 5' to 3'. Since the original double strand is antiparallel, polymerization occurs in opposite directions on each strand at a replication fork. Nucleotides are incorporated as they form hydrogen bonds with their complementary base pairs and covalent phosphodiester bonds with their adjacent nucleotides.

The strand synthesized in the same direction as the movement of the replication fork is the *leading strand*, and the strand synthesized in a direction opposite the movement of the replication fork is the *lagging strand*. DNA polymerase (III or γ) can continuously polymerize DNA as the template unzips without detaching from the template, hence the continuous nature of the leading strand. However, DNA polymerase must repeatedly detach and reattach to remain in the proximity of the moving replication fork on the lagging strand. This action produces distinct fragments of new DNA on the lagging strand each time the polymerase detaches and reattaches, known as *Okazaki fragments*. In prokaryotes, Okazaki fragments are 1,000–2,000 nucleotides, while there are 150–200 nucleotides in eukaryotes.

Okazaki fragments each have their RNA primer, later replaced with DNA by *DNA polymerase I*. This polymerase can remove the ribonucleotides ahead of it while it synthesizes DNA to replace them. Since polymerases cannot connect separate fragments, *DNA ligase* connects the DNA sugar-phosphate backbones of adjacent Okazaki fragments. This enzyme is necessary because other polymerases can only add a free dNTP to a 3'–OH end but cannot connect the ends of nucleotides that have already been incorporated.

Ligase seals the DNA backbone between Okazaki fragments or when a repair mechanism replaces any nucleotides.

In summary:

1. Helicase uncoils and separates the DNA strands.

2. Primase adds RNA primers to which DNA polymerase III can bind.

3. DNA polymerase III begins polymerizing new DNA strands 5' to 3'.

4. Deoxyribonucleoside triphosphates lose two phosphate groups during incorporation, becoming typical nucleotides (sugar + base + phosphate).

5. The leading DNA strand is synthesized continuously.

6. The lagging DNA strand is synthesized in fragments (Okazaki fragments).

7. DNA polymerase I replace the RNA primers with DNA.

8. DNA ligase joins Okazaki fragments together into a continuous DNA strand.

Multiple origins of replication and Okazaki fragments

The average human chromosome contains 140 million nucleotide pairs, and the replication forks proceed at about 50 base pairs per second.

At this rate, the replication process takes about a month, but since there are many replication origins on the eukaryotic chromosome, the process takes hours.

Replication begins at some origins earlier than others, but as replication nears completion, the replication bubbles meet and fuse to form two new DNA molecules.

DNA replication occurs in the S phase of interphase and must be completed before a cell can divide (e.g., mitosis or meiosis). Drugs with molecules similar to the four nucleotides (i.e., nucleotide analogs) are used by patients to inhibit cell division of rapidly dividing cancer cells.

There are many origins of replication in linear DNA of eukaryotes, and several replication forks are formed simultaneously, forming several replication bubbles.

Accordingly, the Okazaki fragments in eukaryotes are shorter (100 – 200 nucleotides), while Okazaki fragments in prokaryotes are longer (1,000 – 2,000 nucleotides). Replication occurs twenty times faster in prokaryotes than in eukaryotes, which undergo more proofreading during DNA replication.

Telomeres as repeating ends of DNA molecules

DNA polymerase adds nucleotides to a 3' –OH end of a preexisting polynucleotide, i.e., it cannot synthesize *de novo*. This is not an issue for circular DNA in prokaryotes, but it is a problem for synthesizing the lagging strand at the ends of linear DNA in eukaryotes.

Although primase can add an RNA primer to the end of the DNA molecule on the lagging strand, DNA polymerase I cannot replace DNA without RNA primers and cannot perform *de novo* synthesis.

The RNA segment and its complementary DNA on the opposite strand would be degraded since chromosomes are regulated to consist of complementary DNA. This leads to degradation of the RNA nucleotides of about 8-12 nucleotides at the ends of DNA strands after each round of replication, eventually encroaching on essential genes on chromosomes and leading to cell death.

Telomeres are the end pieces of each chromosome. There are two telomeres on each of the 46 human chromosomes, which add to 92 telomeres. Their repetitive sequences and associated proteins protect the ends from degradation and allow DNA ends to be replicated without losing important sequences when the RNA primer initiates replication along the leading strand.

In the 1980s, telomeres were proposed to create special segments of DNA synthesized by the telomerase enzyme. This enzyme essentially lengthens the ends of DNA with repeating sequences, usually TTAGGG in humans and other vertebrates. The problem with terminal degradation of DNA still occurs, but since extra sequences have been added during embryogenesis and in stem cells, no essential information is lost. In healthy adult cells, telomerase is off.

Telomerase extends the chromosome ends

The telomerase enzyme carries an internal RNA template. It attaches to the end of the DNA molecule and extends the 3' end with additional DNA. The new DNA added is complementary to the internal RNA template on the enzyme.

This new DNA is added during embryogenesis, leading and lagging strand synthesis as normal. A portion of the telomere is lost with each replication cycle during the organism's lifetime.

Since a double-stranded break is indicative of DNA damage, telomeres have developed associated proteins that inhibit the cell's ability to recognize DNA damage, thereby preventing the unwanted activation of repair mechanisms, cell-cycle arrest, or apoptosis.

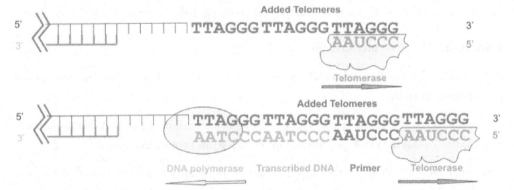

Telomerase has an internal RNA template for complementary DNA synthesis to extend the ends of chromosomes

DNA repair mechanisms during replication

The accuracy of DNA replication cannot be attributed solely to base-pairing specificity, which has an error rate of 1 out of 10^5 base pairs. This rate is not consistent with the observed error rate of 1 in 10^9 base pairs. To arrive at this fidelity, errors during replication must be repaired, the first of which is *proofreading* and performed by DNA polymerases.

DNA polymerase is an aggregate of subunits that combine to form an active *holoenzyme* complex. These aggregates often catalyze more than one reaction. When polymerases inevitably make polymerization errors, DNA polymerase I and III use proofreading to make corrections.

DNA polymerase I and III have 3' to 5' exonuclease activity. When these polymerases incorporate an incorrect nucleotide into the strand (does not base pair correctly with the complementary strand), the exonuclease subunit breaks the phosphodiester bond at the 5' end, excises the nucleotide, and the polymerase subunit inserts the correct nucleotide.

Since polymerases synthesize in the 5' to 3' direction, this excision is named for the complementary strand's 3' to 5' direction.

In addition to 3' to 5' exonuclease activity, DNA polymerase I (but not III) has a 5' to 3' exonuclease. This enzymatic activity allows DNA polymerase I to remove nucleotides ahead of it while synthesizing a new strand simultaneously (5' to 3' polymerization).

This is the basis by which DNA polymerase I excises ribonucleotides in the RNA primers and replaces them with DNA.

This coupling of 5' to 3' exonuclease activity with 5' to 3' polymerization is *nick translation*. A single-stranded cut (nick) essentially translates along the strand as the sequence is replaced with new nucleotides.

When repairs are made, ligase must seal the nicks with phosphodiester bonds in the backbone.

DNA mismatch repair mechanisms

In addition to proofreading, mismatch repair and excision repair are two standard systems that correct errors in DNA.

In *mismatch repair*, a group of enzymes detects a mismatched base pair in a double-stranded DNA molecule that the DNA polymerase proofreading mechanism has missed.

The repair enzyme decides which DNA strand is the template (parent) strand of the new (daughter) DNA molecule by recognizing methylation sites.

Newly synthesized DNA is unmethylated; therefore, the base on the unmethylated strand must be the mismatched base. Since complete methylation is eventually reached after a period, mismatch repair is most accurate immediately after DNA synthesis.

Base-excision and nucleotide excision repair

Base-excision repair (BER) and *nucleotide-excision repair* (NER) act on bases with a mutated structure rather than mismatched base pairs.

BER generally works on small mutations. The excision of the damaged base occurs through breakage of the phosphodiester backbone at the resulting abasic site, and gap-filling by DNA polymerase replaces the base.

BER is accomplished through the concerted effort of a collection of many enzymes (DNA glycosylases, apurinic/apyrimidinic endonucleases, phosphatases, phosphodiesterases, kinases, polymerases, and ligases).

Nucleotide-excision repair is similar, but it is for mutations that seriously affect the helical structure.

NER usually replaces a larger DNA region rather than a single nucleotide or a small patch, as in BER.

For example, DNA exposure to UV light may distort the DNA structure, potentially causing problems during replication, resulting in a pre-cancerous state.

This is why UV (i.e., sunlight) exposure is linked to higher occurrences of skin cancer.

NER recognizes the damage, removes the offending stretch of single-stranded DNA, and polymerizes new DNA using the remaining sequence as a template.

During replication in bacteria, damage can accumulate so extensively that the NER system cannot keep up, and the *SOS repair system* is activated. SOS repair involves the induction of low-fidelity polymerases to prevent the normal high-fidelity polymerases from getting stuck along the DNA strand during synthesis.

Notes for active learning

Genetic Code

The central dogma of molecular biology

The *central dogma* of molecular biology (i.e., DNA → RNA → protein) describes the flow of genetic information in living systems. It states that information flows from DNA to mRNA to protein. DNA is *transcribed* by RNA polymerase to create mRNA molecules, and ribosomes translate mRNA to produce the polypeptide chains comprising proteins.

The central dogma identifies DNA and RNA as information intermediates; information can flow back and forth between DNA and RNA (exemplified by retroviruses, where reverse transcriptase catalyzes DNA formation from RNA) but identifies the protein as a pathway product.

A protein sequence does not act as a template for the synthesis of DNA or RNA.

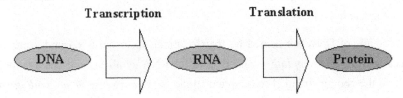

The central dogma of the flow of genetic information

Genes encode proteins

DNA is responsible for the genotype or genetic makeup of an organism. Classical geneticists classify a gene as any of the particles of inheritance on a chromosome. Molecular biologists describe a gene as a sequence of DNA nucleotide bases that encodes for a protein.

Protein is responsible for the phenotype or observable characteristics (e.g., the organism's physical, physiological, developmental, or behavioral traits). Phenotypes result from the actions of enzymes and biological catalysts (mostly proteins) that regulate biological functions. Any alteration of the processes in the central dogma of molecular biology may affect proteins' formation and affect the phenotype.

In the early 1900s, English physician Sir Archibald Garrod introduced the phrase *inborn error of metabolism*, in which inherited defects could be caused by the lack of an enzyme in a metabolic pathway. Garrod suggested a link between genes and proteins, knowing that enzymes are proteins.

In 1940, George Beadle and Edward Tatum x-rayed spores of red bread mold *Neurospora crassa*. They discovered that some cultures lacked a particular enzyme for growth on the medium, and soon after, they found that a single gene was mutated, which resulted in the lack of this single enzyme. From their experiments, they proposed the *one gene-one enzyme hypothesis*, which states that one gene specifies the synthesis of one enzyme.

Later experiments built on this hypothesis. In 1949, biochemists Linus Pauling and Harvey Itano compared hemoglobin in red blood cells of persons with sickle-cell anemia with those of unafflicted individuals. Using electrophoresis to separate molecules by weight and charge, they discovered that the chemical properties of the chain of sickle-cell hemoglobin protein differed from the normal hemoglobin. Years later, biologist Vernon Ingram showed that the biochemical change to the sickle-cell hemoglobin chain was due to substituting a nonpolar valine amino acid for the negatively charged glutamate amino acid. Pauling and Itano proposed the *one gene-one polypeptide hypothesis*, which states that each gene specifies one polypeptide of a protein (proteins may contain multiple polypeptide chains). This hypothesis clarified the earlier one gene-one enzyme hypothesis.

The two strands of DNA are named by their relationship to the RNA and protein that their sequences lead to. The *template strand* is used for RNA synthesis and has a complementary sequence to the coding strand. The template strand is the *antisense or anticoding strand, and the coding strand is the sense strand.* The *coding strand* has an identical sequence to the transcribed RNA but substitutes thymine for uracil.

Messenger RNA is complementary to DNA

RNA (ribonucleic acid) is a nucleic acid that carries a complimentary copy of the genetic code of DNA and is translated into the amino acid sequence of proteins.

Unlike DNA, RNA a $2'-OH$ sugar on the ribose instead of deoxyribose ($2'-H$), and the pyrimidine base uracil replaces thymine. RNA generally does not form helices.

Messenger RNA (mRNA) is a single-stranded piece of RNA containing the bases complementary to the original DNA strand.

The mRNA transcript is synthesized in the nucleus, but after *processing,* it is transported into the cytoplasm, where ribosomes are located. The ribosomes *translate* the mRNA sequence into amino acids and synthesize the polypeptide chains of proteins.

RNA, like DNA, can be replicated in special cases. However, a single-stranded RNA template must be used to synthesize a complementary strand. The new strand must serve as a template for another round of synthesis to create an additional RNA molecule identical to the first template.

Codon–anticodon relationship

Ribosomes read the RNA containing information to synthesize protein as a series of base triplets known as *codons*. The three bases of each codon determine the amino acid incorporated into the growing polypeptide as the ribosome moves along the mRNA transcript.

Each amino acid is added to the polypeptide chain, linked by peptide bonds between the amino acids. After the completed polypeptide dissociates from the ribosome, special modifications and three-dimensional folding occur (in the ribosome for eukaryotic cells) to form the functional protein.

From the four types of ribonucleotide bases (adenine, cytosine, guanine, uracil), there are $4^3 = 64$ codons possible from a series of three ribonucleotides. However, with few exceptions, 20 naturally-occurring amino acids make up an organism's proteins.

In this way, the code is *degenerate;* more than one codon may specify the same amino acid.

In 1961, Marshall Nirenberg and J. Heinrich Matthaei assembled the initial relationships between naturally occurring amino acids and the codons that specify them. They found that an enzyme is used to construct synthetic RNA in a cell-free system.

By translating three ribonucleotides at a time and observing the amino acid incorporated, they began to decipher the triplet code. This demonstrated the role of nucleotides in protein synthesis.

Three nucleotides (codons) specify a single amino acid.

Initiation and termination codons

The 64 codons include 4 special codons. AUG (start codon) codes for methionine and signals the start of translation on an RNA transcript, forming the first amino acid in the nascent polypeptide.

Three other codons, UAG, UGA, and UAA, do not encode for any amino acid but signal a ribosome to terminate translation.

Although the code is degenerate (a single amino acid is specified by more than one codon), it is *unambiguous*: each nucleotide triplet encodes a single amino acid.

The amino acid sequence of a peptide encoded by a nucleotide sequence can be determined from the genetic code.

For example, AUG–CAU–UAC–UAA encodes for: Met–His–Tyr–Stop.

Additionally, the degeneracy of the genetic code is observed in the table.

For example, CCC, CCU, CCA, and CCG encode for the amino acid proline.

Second letter

		U	C	A	G	
First letter	**U**	UUU ⎤ Phe UUC ⎦ UUA ⎤ Leu UUG ⎦	UCU ⎤ UCC ⎥ Ser UCA ⎥ UCG ⎦	UAU ⎤ Tyr UAC ⎦ UAA **Stop** UAG **Stop**	UGU ⎤ Cys UGC ⎦ UGA **Stop** UGG Trp	U C A G
	C	CUU ⎤ CUC ⎥ Leu CUA ⎥ CUG ⎦	CCU ⎤ CCC ⎥ Pro CCA ⎥ CCG ⎦	CAU ⎤ His CAC ⎦ CAA ⎤ Gln CAG ⎦	CGU ⎤ CGC ⎥ Arg CGA ⎥ CGG ⎦	U C A G
	A	AUU ⎤ AUC ⎥ Ile AUA ⎦ AUG Met	ACU ⎤ ACC ⎥ Thr ACA ⎥ ACG ⎦	AAU ⎤ Asn AAC ⎦ AAA ⎤ Lys AAG ⎦	AGU ⎤ Ser AGC ⎦ AGA ⎤ Arg AGG ⎦	U C A G
	G	GUU ⎤ GUC ⎥ Val GUA ⎥ GUG ⎦	GCU ⎤ GCC ⎥ Ala GCA ⎥ GCG ⎦	GAU ⎤ Asp GAC ⎦ GAA ⎤ Glu GAG ⎦	GGU ⎤ GGC ⎥ Gly GGA ⎥ GGG ⎦	U C A G

(Third letter)

Genetic code with 3 nucleotides specifying an amino acid

Mutations change the DNA sequence

A genetic mutation is a permanent change in the sequence of DNA nucleotide bases, evading proofreading and repair mechanisms.

Major types of mutations include *point mutations*, in which a single base is replaced; *additions*, in which sections of DNA are added; and *deletions*, in which sections of DNA are deleted. The result is the potential for a misread in the DNA nucleotide code or the loss of a gene.

Mutations are categorized by their effect; *nonsense* mutations, *missense* mutations, *silent* mutations, *neutral* mutations, and *frameshift* mutations.

Mutations have consequences that range from no effect to the inactivation of a protein's function.

At some point mutations, the corresponding change in the RNA causes a change in the resulting polypeptide. For example, a DNA sequence <u>C</u>CA mutated to <u>T</u>CA causes the RNA codon <u>G</u>GU for glycine to be changed to the <u>A</u>GU codon for serine. In this case, a single nucleotide change has caused a single amino acid change.

Missense mutations cause codons to specify different amino acids.

Nonsense mutations cause a codon that specifies for an amino acid to change to a stop codon, which results in a truncated (often nonfunctional) protein.

Mutations can result in nonfunctional proteins, and a single nonfunctioning protein can have dramatic effects. However, not all DNA mutations lead to changes in the resulting protein.

For example, a DNA sequence <u>G</u>AT mutated to <u>G</u>AA causes the RNA codon <u>C</u>UA to change to <u>C</u>UU; both codons translate the same amino acid, leucine.

A *silent mutation* cannot be observed in the organism's phenotype (i.e., protein sequence).

A *neutral mutation* neither benefits nor inhibits the function of an organism. For example, a mutation leading to an amino acid change from aspartic acid to glutamic acid, which has negatively-charged side chains, may not cause a major structural or functional change in a protein. In this example, the organism may be unaffected by the amino acid change. Silent mutations are essentially neutral mutations unless some mechanism is affected, depending specifically on the DNA or corresponding amino acid sequence.

There are several ways a mutation may not negatively affect the organism. For example, mutations within introns (segments excised when mRNA is processed) may not affect the functional protein. Proteins may be unaffected by an amino acid change, especially if the new amino acid has similar properties.

If a gene is damaged, there may be no adverse effect on the organism if the paired chromosome's homologous gene can produce an intact protein. Damage to genes that synthesize amino acids may not affect the organism if that amino acid is obtained from an external source, such as the medium a bacterium is growing on.

Mutations can result in nonfunctional proteins, and even a single nonfunctioning protein can have dramatic effects. For example, phenylketonuria is a disease that results when the enzyme that breaks down phenylalanine is nonfunctional, causing phenylalanine to build up in the system. Albinism is caused by a faulty enzyme elsewhere in the same pathway. Cystic fibrosis results from the inheritance of a change in a chloride transport protein in the plasma membrane. A faulty receptor for male sex hormones causes androgen insensitivity in men, where the body's cells cannot respond to testosterone and instead develop like a female, even though all the cells have XY sex chromosomes.

Sickle cell anemia results from a single base change in the DNA: in the hemoglobin polypeptide chain, a glutamate amino acid is changed to valine at the sixth residue of the β-chain, distorting the structure of red blood cells into a sickle shape. The malformed red blood cells break down at a faster rate, causing anemia (low red blood cell count), and can become lodged within small vessels (capillaries), causing ischemia (restriction in blood supply).

A *frameshift mutation* alters the triplet reading frame so that codons downstream from the mutation are out of register and not read correctly. They occur when one or more nucleotides are inserted or deleted, resulting in a new sequence of codons and nonfunctional proteins; it may affect the position of the stop codon.

For example, if there is a mRNA sequence GAC CCG UAU corresponding to aspartic acid, proline, and tyrosine, deletion of the first amino acid causes a frameshift mutation. The mutated mRNA sequence would be ACC CGU AU, and it now encodes for threonine and arginine. The human transposon *Alu* causes hemophilia when a frameshift mutation leads to a premature stop codon in the gene for clotting factor IX.

Spontaneous mutations occur randomly but are rare due to imperfections in the replication machinery.

Mutagens are environmental agents that produce changes in DNA. Many mutagens are carcinogens or cancer-causing agents. Proofreading and other repair mechanisms lower the likelihood of mutation to one out of a billion base pairs replicated, but high exposure to mutagens may increase this rate.

If a mutation occurs in a somatic cell (cell other than an egg or sperm), it affects the individual organism and can cause cancer conditions. Future generations can inherit mutations in germ cells (sperm or egg cells) and cause genetic diseases; more than 4,000 genetic diseases have been identified.

Exogenous mutagens and transposons

Radiation is a common mutagen. X-rays and gamma rays are ionizing radiation that creates dangerous free radicals (i.e., atoms with unpaired electrons), and ultraviolet (UV) radiation can cause pyrimidines (thymine or cytosine) to form covalent linkages as pyrimidine dimers. Cellular repair enzymes must remove it. A lack of these enzymes causes xeroderma pigmentosum, which leads to a higher incidence of skin cancer.

Organic chemicals can act directly on DNA. The mutagen 5-bromouracil pairs with thymine, so the A–T base pair becomes a G–C base pair. Other chemicals may add hydrocarbon groups or remove amino groups from DNA bases. Tobacco smoke contains chemical carcinogens.

A chemical mutagen is sodium nitrite ($NaNO_2$), a preservative in processed meats. In the presence of amines, sodium nitrite forms nitrosamines, which assist in converting the base cytosine into uracil.

Transposons are DNA sequences that can move within and between chromosomes and cause mutations when they change the DNA sequence. These "jumping genes" were proposed by Barbara McClintock and first detected in maize (corn). Now transposons have been observed in bacteria, fruit flies, and other organisms.

Charcot-Marie-Tooth disease is a rare human disorder where muscles and nerves of legs and feet wither away. It is believed to result from a transposon that caused the partial duplication of a chromosome, giving the patient three copies of a series of genes, leading to the breakdown of myelin (insulating sheath around neurons) and thus affecting nerve transmission. Viruses can cause mutations when they integrate their DNA into the host genome.

Transcription of DNA into mRNA

mRNA structure and function

Messenger RNA (mRNA) is the single-stranded RNA transcript comprising the nucleotide sequence information to synthesize polypeptides. It is different from tRNA or rRNA because it has a modified guanine (7-methylguanosine) base 5' cap and a series of adenine nucleotides as a 3' poly-A tail. 5' capping occurs early before the RNA polymerase is finished transcribing RNA.

The cap is used by a ribosome for attachment to begin translation; it provides stability for the mRNA molecule. The polyadenylation at the 3' end of the transcript creates the poly-A tail of approximately 150-200 adenine (A) nucleotides.

This is *template-independent* because it does not require a template strand for the polymerization to occur. This tail inhibits the degradation of mRNA in the cytoplasm by hydrolytic enzymes.

Delay of degradation allows the mRNA to remain in the cell cytoplasm for longer, leading to more polypeptides translated from the same transcript. Polyadenylation can occur in prokaryotes, but it instead promotes degradation.

The region between the 5' cap and the mRNA start codon is the 5' untranslated region (5'–UTR). Similarly, the region between the mRNA stop codon and the poly-A tail is the 3'–UTR. Although UTRs are not translated, they function for stability and localization of the pre-processed mRNA (pre-mRNA, heterogeneous nuclear RNA, or hnRNA).

mRNA structure, including the untranslated regions (UTRs)

mRNA processing in eukaryotes

In eukaryotes, the newly-formed RNA (*primary transcript RNA* or *pre-RNA*) is processed before leaving the nucleus as a *mature RNA*. Processing involves capping and polyadenylation (described above).

Additional processing that must occur during the formation of the mature RNA molecule is the splicing of the *introns*, the non-coding RNA regions that must be excised. The *exons* are the coding regions that remain in the final transcript.

After the introns are excised, the exons are joined in the process of *RNA splicing*.

47

mRNA exons are eventually translated into polypeptides after leaving the nucleus. The organization of genes into introns and exons is of evolutionary importance.

Exons generally represent functional protein domains, so splicing and exon composition changes allow the easy shuffling of protein domains to create new proteins.

Splicing differs during developmental (i.e., fetus, adult) or tissue-specific (e.g., lung, heart).

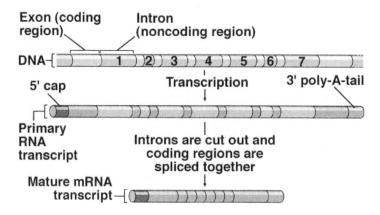

mRNA with introns removed and exons ligated

An exception for RNA processing involves mitochondria, which have the complete set of machinery needed to produce their proteins, and their circular DNA molecules (like prokaryotes) lack introns.

DNA is not always transcribed into mRNA; it produces other types of RNA such as *transfer RNA* (tRNA) or *ribosomal RNA* (rRNA). tRNA molecules travel out of the nucleus after transcription, where they are "activated" when a tRNA synthetase enzyme attaches the corresponding amino acid.

rRNAs (synthesized in the nucleolus within the nucleus), along with various proteins, form the subunits of ribosomes before the subunits migrate out of the nucleus into the cytoplasm.

Histones and mechanism of transcription

Transcription (DNA → RNA) transforms the information in stable DNA into dynamic mRNA, a necessary component for protein production.

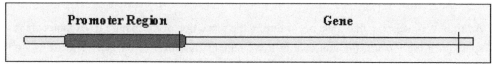

A segment of DNA with upstream promoter region
where RNA polymerase binds to initiate transcription

Transcription takes place in the nucleus, where DNA to be transcribed adopts an "open" conformation, uncoiling and thus exposing the template strand.

DNA is usually tightly bound to histones, but the binding of histone deacetylases causes a conformational change in the DNA-histone complex, allowing the association to become loose and open. In an open conformation, exposed DNA promoter regions are likely to be recognized by transcription factors.

The *promoter* is regions on DNA where the RNA polymerase binds to begin transcription of mRNA. Promoters are often 30, 75, and 90 nucleotide base pairs upstream (towards the 5' end) from the *transcription start site* (TSS), where transcription begins.

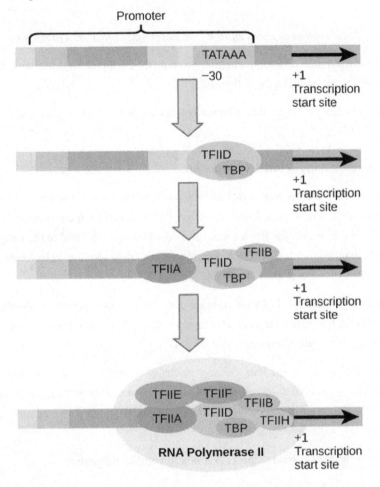

RNA transcription is influenced by transcription factors that increase the affinity of the RNA polymerase and the rate of mRNA synthesis as enhancers or decrease the rate as inhibitors

RNA polymerase uncoils DNA to expose the template strand and processes from 3' to 5' along the DNA, incorporating free ribonucleotide triphosphates (NTPs) into the growing mRNA strand NTPs (i.e., ATP, CTP, GTP, or UTP) become ribonucleotides. Since RNA polymerase moves from the 3' to the 5' end of a DNA template sequence, the RNA transcript is synthesized in a 5' to 3' direction (same as in DNA synthesis), which requires a free 3'−OH end.

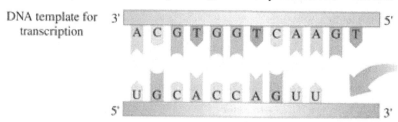

The direction of transcription with bases added to 3' end of mRNA

The mRNA strand is complementary to the DNA template and the same as the DNA coding strand (except uracil replaces thymine).

Phosphodiester bonds link ribonucleotides as is DNA, but with ribose instead of deoxyribose in DNA.

RNA polymerase catalyzes mRNA formation

RNA polymerization creates transcripts that must dissociate from the template DNA. A short portion of the RNA is base-paired with the DNA for the correct sequence to be polymerized, but otherwise, the 5' end of the RNA transcript is not hydrogen-bonded to the template strand of the DNA double-strand. The DNA strands reform their double helix once the newly synthesized RNA dissociates from the DNA.

Unlike DNA polymerase III, RNA polymerase does not require a primer to initiate synthesis; the stretch of DNA template strand encodes for a single RNA transcript is the *transcription unit* (i.e., promoter, RNA-coding sequence, and terminator).

In addition to the promoter and TSS, eukaryotes can contain a *TATA box* (or *Hogness box*) in their promoter, specialized thymine, and adenine nucleotides sequence. Eukaryotic transcription requires particular proteins, or *transcription factors*, to control and enable transcription.

Many transcription factors bind at the TATA box to regulate transcription.

Not all genes have a TATA box.

The *transcription initiation complex* is the complete assembly of transcription factors and RNA polymerase bound to the DNA.

Prokaryotes do not require transcription factors; the RNA polymerase recognizes the promoter and begins transcription. *Pribnow box* is a sequence in their promoter similar to the TATA box.

Termination of transcription

Termination of transcription occurs when RNA polymerization ends, and the RNA transcript is released from the DNA coding strand. Termination in prokaryotes occurs when the RNA polymerase transcribes the *terminator* sequence. Termination is not well understood in eukaryotes, but it includes various protein factors interacting with the DNA strand and the RNA polymerase.

Transcription in eukaryotes usually proceeds at least 30 base pairs after the RNA stop codon, and termination usually occurs in two ways.

Intrinsic termination is where specific sequences, the *termination sites* create a stem-loop in the RNA that causes the RNA to dissociate from the DNA template strand.

The second mechanism is *rho (ρ) dependent termination*, where the ρ protein factor travels along the synthesized RNA and dislodges the RNA polymerase off the DNA template strand.

Multiple RNA polymerases transcribe the same template

Cells produce thousands of copies of the same RNA transcripts. Since many transcripts are available for translation, protein synthesis occurs more quickly than if translation occurs along a single mRNA.

In prokaryotes and eukaryotes, multiple RNA polymerases transcribe the same template simultaneously.

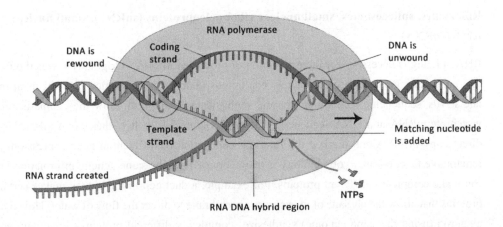

RNA polymerase synthesizes a single strand of RNA complementary to the DNA template strand

Summary of transcription

1. RNA polymerase binds to the promoter region on the DNA, initiating transcription.

2. RNA polymerase uncoils and separates the DNA strands as it synthesizes the RNA strand in a 5' to 3' direction.

3. One DNA strand is used as a template (antisense strand). The other strand (coding strand) is not used but has the same sequence as the RNA transcript (sense strand), except with thymine (in DNA) instead of uracil (in RNA).

4. Free nucleoside triphosphates (NTP) are incorporated, losing two of their phosphates. The new RNA nucleotides temporarily form base pairs with the template DNA.

5. The terminator sequence causes the RNA polymerase to stop transcription and separate from the DNA, and the DNA rewinds.

6. RNA destined for protein translation is messenger RNA (mRNA).

7. mRNA processes in the nucleus with splicing (remove introns and join exons), adding 5' G–cap and 3' poly–A tail.

8. Processed mRNA migrates through nuclear pores into the cytoplasm for protein translation.

Ribozymes, spliceosomes, small nuclear ribonucleoproteins (snRNP), small nuclear RNA (snRNA)

RNA splicing is necessary for the production of processed mRNA. Originally it was thought that eukaryotic genomes are completely continuous (as bacterial genomes). However, in the late 1970s, sequencing technology became sophisticated enough to allow the comparison of vertebrate mRNA and DNA sequences. The results replaced the hypothesis that mRNA is a direct copy of DNA and marked the first real conception of differential gene expression. A remarkable facet of eukaryotic biology is that every cell has the same genetic information but can make completely different proteins. For example, a duct cell in the kidney makes certain proteins that allow the passage of ions across a membrane to direct the flow of water. However, a neuron (using the same genome) synthesizes completely different proteins to maintain and harness a membrane potential.

Splicing does not often decide cell fate, but it does allow for the synthesis of different proteins from the same DNA template by ligating (joining) exons and removing introns. *Small nuclear RNA* (snRNA) are special types of RNA that combine with proteins to form *small nuclear ribonucleoproteins* (snRNPs), which make up *spliceosomes*, the complexes that perform RNA splicing. The spliceosome recognizes splice sites (exon and intron boundaries) and enzymatically forms stretches of RNA as *lariats* from the intron sequences. The lariat is then cleaved from the transcript, and the remaining exons are ligated together. Splicing, like all mRNA processing, occurs in the nucleus, separate from the ribosomes. After the RNA is fully processed, it is exported from the nucleus via nuclear pores into the cytoplasm to be translated. Splicing does not occur in bacteria since they do not have introns; instead, translation often occurs immediately after transcription since both processes are in the nucleus.

Alternative splicing allows an array of unique mRNAs to be generated from the same primary RNA transcript. A change in the splice recognition site can cause a putative exon in a different transcript to become an intron in another transcript (i.e., cell type or stage of development). In this way, different proteins can be constructed by shuffling exons. This is done by selectively removing parts of a primary RNA transcript and arranging different combinations; as a result, each mRNA encodes for a different protein product.

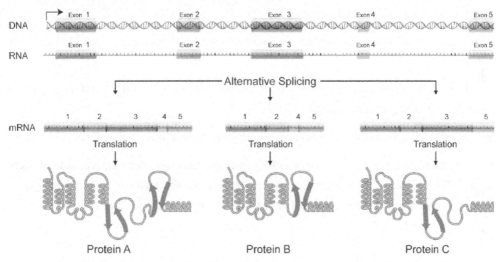

DNA alternative splicing allows the same genome to transcribe tissue
or developmentally-specific proteins for specific functions

In 1989, American scientists Sidney Altman and Thomas Cech were awarded the Nobel Prize for discovering that some RNA molecules have an enzymatic function. *Ribozymes* are RNA molecules that include the snRNA involved in RNA splicing and the RNA molecules in the protozoan *Tetrahymena*, which catalyze condensation and hydrolysis of phosphodiester bonds. It is postulated that RNA has served as both the genetic material and enzymes in early life forms. The ribozyme suggests that RNA is the answer to the persistent uncertainty about whether DNA or RNA came first in evolutionary history.

Functional and evolutionary significance of introns

The role of RNA non-coding (intronic) regions of the genome is still contested.

Molecular biology is moving to understand that these regions are important in regulating gene products.

Intron sequences often contain short stretches of RNA, known as small interfering RNA (siRNA), which significantly affect regulating gene expression.

The evolutionary importance of the noncontinuity of the genome is controversial.

Some researchers assert that because spliceosome-splicing is not conserved in prokaryotes, it has limited importance to species' origin.

However, others hypothesize that the ability to shuffle genes is important to the evolution of unique phenotypes within a population.

Introns can provide significant evolutionary advantages, mainly because they enable alternative splicing.

For example, the thyroid and pituitary glands use the same primary mRNA transcript but, via alternative splicing, produce different proteins.

Investigators have found that the simpler the eukaryote, the less likely is the presence of introns.

Though introns are mostly restricted to eukaryotes, an intron has been discovered in the gene for a tRNA molecule in the cyanobacterium *Anabaena*; this intron is *self-splicing* (like a ribozyme) and capable of splicing itself out of an RNA transcript.

Translation Synthesizes Proteins from mRNA

mRNA and ribonucleases

Messenger RNA (mRNA) molecules containing information transcribed from DNA are transported into the cytosol from the nucleus after processing (i.e., 5' cap, 3' poly-A tail, and splicing – the removal of introns and ligation of exons). The mRNA contains the information necessary for ribosomes to assemble amino acids into polypeptides, the building blocks of proteins.

Translational control occurs in the cytoplasm after mRNA leaves the nucleus, but before there is a protein product. The life expectancy of mRNA molecules and their ability to bind ribosomes can vary.

The longer an active mRNA molecule remains in the cytoplasm; the more proteins are synthesized. mRNAs may need additional changes before they are translated.

Ribonucleases are enzymes that degrade RNA (e.g., mRNA). Mature mRNA molecules contain a 5'–cap and 3'–poly-A tail, non-coding segments that influence how long the mRNA can avoid being degraded by ribonucleases.

Translational controls

An example of translational control in mature mammalian red blood cells that eject their nucleus but synthesize hemoglobin protein for several months, so the mRNAs in red blood cells must persist during this time since no additional RNA is transcribed.

Another example of translational control involves frog eggs with mRNA as "masked messengers" not translated until fertilization occurs. When fertilization of the frog egg occurs, the mRNA is "unmasked," and there is a rapid synthesis of proteins.

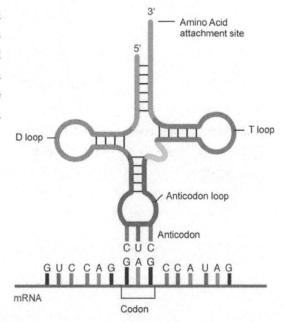

Transfer RNA interprets codons

Transfer RNA (tRNA) is the interpreter of the codons on the mRNA. tRNA associate each three-nucleotide anticodon with amino acids and transfer the corresponding amino acid to the growing polypeptides.

tRNA carries a single amino acid on its 3' end and has an anticodon segment.

An *anticodon* (contained within the *anticodon loop*) is a special three-nucleotide sequence on the tRNA molecule that base-pairs with a complementary three-nucleotide codon on the mRNA.

After a tRNA activated with amino acid base pairs (*via* hydrogen bonds) with a codon, the ribosome incorporates the amino acid into the growing polypeptide.

The tRNA, now free from the amino acid, which is part of the growing polypeptide, dissociates and returns to the cytoplasm, ready to become charged by binding another specific amino acid at its 3'− end.

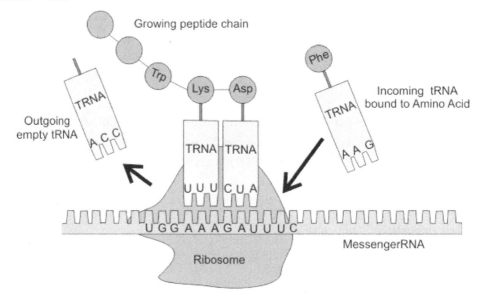

Peptide synthesis using codons on mRNA and anticodons on tRNA with associated amino acids

tRNA as anticodons

There are many tRNAs with anticodons complementary to codons.

A tRNA-activating enzyme (aminoacyl tRNA synthetase) charges the 3'−end of a tRNA with the correct amino acid, an *aminoacylation* process.

Twenty tRNA-activating enzymes corresponding to each of the 20 unique amino acids.

The chemical properties and three-dimensional structures of each tRNA allow the tRNA-activating enzymes to recognize their tRNA.

When the amino acid is attached to the tRNA molecule, a high-energy bond is created using ATP.

The energy stored from this high-energy bond transfers and binds the amino acids to the growing polypeptide chain during translation.

A recent analysis of entire genomes revealed that some organisms do not have genes for all twenty aminoacyl-tRNA synthetases. They do, however, use all twenty amino acids to construct their proteins.

The solution, as is often the case in living cells, is that more complex mechanisms are used. For instance, some bacteria do not have an enzyme for charging glutamine onto its tRNA. Instead, a single enzyme adds glutamic acid to the glutamic acid tRNA molecules and to the glutamine tRNA molecules. A second enzyme then converts the glutamic acid into glutamine on the latter tRNA molecules, forming the proper pairing of the tRNA with the amino acid.

Wobble position of mRNA

The third base of an mRNA codon is the *wobble position* because of "flexibility" in the third position of codon-anticodon (hydrogen bonding) base pairing.

For example, the base U of a tRNA anticodon in the third position can base pair with A or G. The most versatile tRNA have the modified base inosine (I) in the wobble position because inosine forms hydrogen bonds with U, C, or A.

Wobble explains why degenerate (synonymous) codons for an amino acid differ in the third position.

It allows a tRNA holding an amino acid to potentially bind to multiple codons with a different third base, each encoding for the same amino acid specific to that tRNA.

Ribosomal RNA

Ribosomal RNA (rRNA) is synthesized from a DNA template in the nucleolus (organelle in the nucleus).

Many proteins are transported from their site of synthesis in the cytoplasm into the nucleus, where rRNA and proteins form the small subunit (the 30S for prokaryotes and 40S for eukaryotes) the large subunit (50S for prokaryotes and 60S for eukaryotes) of the complete ribosome.

These two subunits travel out to the cytoplasm through the nuclear pores, where they join to form the complete ribosome (the 70S for prokaryotes and 80S for eukaryotes) when translation occurs.

Each ribosome is composed of dozens of associated proteins.

The "S" stands for Svedberg units, which measures the density and corresponds to the sedimentation value from the particles' configuration.

tRNA and rRNA composition and structure (e.g., RNA nucleotides)

Each tRNA molecule is a single strand containing 75 to 95 nucleotides, and particular sequences on this single strand form base pairs with other parts of the molecule, forming a tightly-compacted T-shaped structure.

Most of the ribonucleotides in tRNA are the normally-occurring RNA bases (A, C, G, and U), but there are some variant bases, such as pseudouridine, that result from modifications (alkylation, methylation, and glycosylation) to the typical bases that occur after RNA transcription. These modified bases, which usually occur in restricted sites of the tRNA molecule, allow for the formation of unusual base pairs.

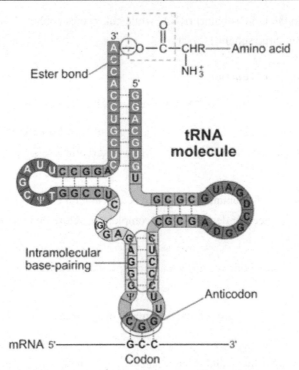

tRNA with amino acid joined at the 3'—OH end, creating a phosphodiester bond

The secondary (two-dimensional) structure of a tRNA molecule resembles a cloverleaf, while the tertiary (three-dimensional) structure is L-shaped. Five regions in tRNA are not base-paired: the CCA acceptor stem, the D-loop, the TΨC loop, the anticodon loop, and the extra arm.

The nucleotide sequence CCA is at the 3'—OH end of the tRNA and allows for the attachment of an amino acid by a phosphodiester bond, creating a charged tRNA. Which amino acid is attached depends on the anticodon, the three-base sequence binding to a complementary triplet codon on the mRNA according to the base-pairing rules.

Each tRNA has a slightly different chemical property and three-dimensional structure, which allows the tRNA-activating enzyme to attach the correct amino acid to the 3'—OH end of the tRNA. The cell's cytoplasm contains all twenty amino acids either by synthesizing them or importing them into the cell.

Ribosomal RNAs, which are structural components of the ribosome, perform critical functions for protein synthesis. rRNAs are synthesized in the nucleolus, while ribosomal proteins are synthesized in the cytoplasm and are brought to the nucleolus to be joined with the rRNAs for the assembly of the two ribosomal subunits: the *large subunit* and the *small subunit*.

The rRNA in the large subunit has ribozyme activity and catalyzes the formation of peptide bonds between adjacent amino acids. The secondary structure of rRNA is extensive, and it plays an important role in recognizing tRNA and mRNA that bind to the ribosome. Secondary rRNA structure has been conserved throughout evolution. Prokaryotes contain 16S (in small subunit),

23S and 5S (both in the large subunit) rRNA, while eukaryotes contain 18S (in small subunit) and 5S, 5.8S, 28S (in large subunit).

Ribosomes structure and function

The ribosome is composed of a few rRNA molecules and many proteins.

The ribosome consists of a small subunit and a large subunit. Prokaryotic ribosomes are the 70S (30S small subunit + 50S large subunit), while eukaryotic ribosomes are 80S (40S small subunit + 60S large subunit).

The Svedberg values for the subunits do not add sedimentation coefficients for the assembled ribosome due to differences in density of the complete structure compared to the individual subunits.

In ribosomes, the ribonucleotides of mRNA are interpreted and synthesized into an amino acid sequence.

The mRNA strand fits into a groove on the small subunit, bases pointing toward the large subunit.

The ribosome acts as a "reader," and when it reaches a termination sequence in the mRNA, the link between the synthesized polypeptide chain and tRNA is broken.

The completed polypeptide is released from the ribosome.

Prokaryotic cells contain about 10,000 ribosomes, and eukaryotic cells contain many more.

Ribosomes have binding sites for mRNA and tRNA molecules.

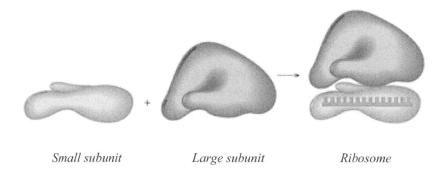

Small subunit　　　*Large subunit*　　　*Ribosome*

Free *vs.* bound ribosomes

Ribosomes can float freely in the cytosol or attach to the endoplasmic reticulum (ER); the *rough ER* is due to its appearance caused by the ribosomes studding its surface.

Prokaryotic cells contain about 10,000 ribosomes, and eukaryotic cells contain many more. Ribosomes have binding sites for mRNA and tRNA molecules.

Free ribosomes synthesize proteins primarily used within the cytosol of the cell.

As small proteins emerge from the ribosome, they undergo folding.

Larger proteins fold within the recess of small, hollow chambers in proteins known as *chaperones*.

Bound ribosomes on the rough endoplasmic reticulum usually synthesize proteins used for the secretory pathway (e.g., secreted from the cell, embedded into membranes, or targeted for organelles).

Multiple ribosomes can simultaneously translate the same mRNA with elongating polypeptides of different lengths in relation to the ribosomes' progress.

A group of ribosomes on a single RNA is a *polyribosome* (polysome).

However, mRNA molecules cannot be translated indefinitely and are eventually degraded into ribonucleotides by cytoplasmic enzymes.

A ribosome has three sites holding a tRNA: the *E* (exit) *site, P* (peptidyl) *site,* and *A* (aminoacyl) *site*.

The E site is the 5' of the mRNA held by the ribosome and the A site on the 3'−side.

The E site holds a discharged tRNA that is ready for dissociation, the P site tRNA holds the growing polypeptide, and the A site tRNA holds the following amino acid to be added to the polypeptide chain.

Initiation and termination co-factors

Translation, the process by which a mRNA nucleotide sequence is read as triplet codons to assemble a polypeptide chain, involves three steps: chain initiation, elongation, and termination. The mRNA codons base pair with the tRNA anticodons, which represent specific amino acids based on the nucleotide sequence.

Enzymes are required for all three steps, and energy is needed for the first two steps. Once the polypeptide is fully formed and translation has terminated, the ribosome then dissociates into its two subunits.

Chain initiation is the first step in translation. Before translation begins, the two subunits of the ribosome are not yet combined. They are assembled separately in the nucleus and travel through the pores of the nuclear envelope and combine in the cytoplasm to form a functional ribosome when translation starts.

Since translation moves 5' to 3' along the mRNA strand, the small subunit first binds the 5' end of the mRNA. The subunit moves along the transcript until it finds the start codon, AUG. The tRNA for AUG (attached amino acid is methionine) hybridizes to the start codon using its anticodon, and the large subunit binds the small subunit, forming the complete ribosome. This first tRNA is the *initiator tRNA*.

Initiation factor proteins drive this initial binding. The activity of these factors regulates the rate of protein synthesis. The initiation phase is the slowest of the three phases of the assembly process.

Chain elongation is the process of adding new amino acids to the growing polypeptide chain. After initiation, the tRNA holding the first amino acid (methionine) is bound to the P site.

The A site is now empty and has an exposed codon for the next amino acid. The tRNA with the appropriate anticodon then binds the A site, which requires hydrolysis of a GTP. Elongation factor proteins facilitate this base pairing.

With the two amino acids on the tRNAs now nearby, the methionine forms a peptide bond with the amino acid held in the A site, dissociating from the tRNA in the P site at the same time. A ribozyme catalyzes this transfer in the large subunit.

The tRNA in the A site now holds two amino acids, with the methionine at the N-terminus (the end with the free amino group) of the growing polypeptide and the newest amino acid attached to the tRNA.

The mRNA transcript now slides through the ribosome, 3 ribonucleotides forward. The tRNA anticodons are still associated with their matching codons, so this movement causes the tRNA to move sites, a process of *translocation*.

The discharged tRNA in the P site moves to the E site, and the tRNA holding the growing polypeptide moves to the P site. The A site is now empty and ready for a charged tRNA to recognize the next codon. As the tRNA holding the next amino acid binds the A site, the discharged tRNA in the E site dissociates away from the ribosome, where it is free to associate to a new amino acid in the cytoplasm.

A peptide bond attaches the newly-arrived amino acid. After translocation, the tRNA attached to the recent amino acid moves into the P site, and the tRNA formerly attached to A site moves to the E site and is released. An amino acid–tRNA complex is in the P site.

This process of elongation continues as more codons on the mRNA move through the ribosome. The growing polypeptide chain elongates and is passed from tRNA to incoming tRNA, and the N-terminus of the polypeptide emerges. This elongation step is rapid and occurs about 15 times per second in *E. coli*.

The elongation repeats until the ribosome eventually reaches one of three stop codons on the mRNA, which leads to *chain termination*. No tRNA anticodons recognize the stop codons; instead, *release factors* bind to the stop codon, causing translation to stop.

This binding causes the addition of a water molecule instead of an amino acid to the polypeptide chain. The polypeptide chain is released, the uncharged tRNA dissociates from the ribosome, and the ribosomal subunits dissociate.

Summary of translation

1. mRNA attaches to a small subunit of the ribosome and binds to a charged tRNA molecule (with an attached amino acid) based on its specific codon sequence.

2. The large subunit of ribosome joins the complex.

3. Initiator tRNA resides in P site of the ribosome, and a new tRNA recognizes the next codon sequence on mRNA and attaches to the A site of the ribosome.

4. A peptide bond is formed between the amino acid attached to the tRNA in the P site and the amino acid attached to the tRNA in the A site.

5. The uncharged tRNA in the P site moves to the E site, where it is then released, and the tRNA in the A site moves to the P site.

6. Another tRNA binds to the A site, and the pattern continues, creating a growing polypeptide chain until a termination codon is reached.

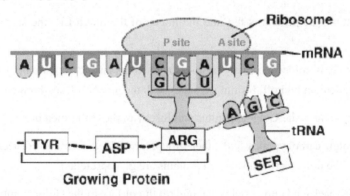

Post-translational modifications of protein

Post-translational control regulates the activity of the protein in the cell after translation. For a polypeptide product of translation to become a functional protein, post-translational modifications are made.

These modifications include bending and twisting the chain into the correct three-dimensional shape (protein folding), sometimes facilitated by chaperone molecules.

The growing polypeptide folds into its tertiary structure, forming disulfide links, salt bridges, or other interactions that make the polypeptide a biologically-active protein.

Other changes include additions to the polypeptide chain, such as carbohydrate or lipid derivatives that may be covalently attached when the functional protein is folded.

The initial amino acid methionine is often removed from the beginning of the polypeptide. Some molecules are composed of multiple polypeptide chains that must be joined to achieve the functional protein (quaternary structure).

Post-translational control may involve degradation to "activate" a protein.

For example, the bovine protein proinsulin is inactive when first translated.

After a sequence of 30 amino acids is removed from the middle of the chain and disulfide bonds join the two pieces, the protein becomes active.

In other cases, proteins are degraded to cause deactivation.

Proteasomes and signal sequence

Proteasomes degrade misfolded, ubiquitinated proteins for amino acid protein recycling

Proteasomes (enzymes that target proteins) are large protein complexes that carry out this task.

For example, cyclins that control the cell cycle are present temporarily and degraded.

Proteins to be secreted from a cell have a signal sequence that binds to a specific membrane protein on the surface of the rough endoplasmic reticulum.

During translation, the protein is fed into the lumen of the rough ER; the signal sequence is removed.

Once the protein is folded correctly in the rough endoplasmic reticulum, portions of the endoplasmic reticulum bud off, forming vesicles with the properly folded protein.

The vesicles migrate to the Golgi apparatus and fuse with the Golgi membrane.

Within the Golgi, carbohydrates and other groups are added or removed according to the destinations of the proteins (most secreted proteins are glycoproteins).

The proteins are packaged into vesicles that bud off the surface of the Golgi membrane and may travel to the plasma membrane (secretory pathway), where they fuse and release their contents in the extracellular fluid through *exocytosis.*

Eukaryotic Chromosome Organization

Histone proteins and supercoiling

Histones are positively charged chromosomal proteins responsible for the compact packing and winding of chromosomal negatively charged DNA. A histone protein octamer and a histone H1 protein (nucleosome) form a protein core around which DNA winds to achieve a compact state.

Nonhistone chromosomal proteins are associated with the chromosomes. They have various functions, such as regulatory and enzymatic roles. An active research area is chromatin remodeling via histones to regulate gene expression within cells.

A chromosome consists of a single DNA molecule wound tightly around thousands of *histone* proteins. The basic unit of compact DNA is a *nucleosome* consisting of negatively charged DNA wound around a positively-charged histone octamer core and held in place by an additional histone H1.

A nucleosome consists of two H2A, two H2B, two H3, two H4, and one H1 histone.

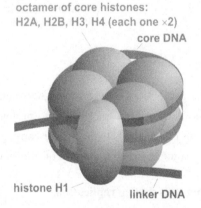

octamer of core histones:
H2A, H2B, H3, H4 (each one ×2)

core DNA

histone H1

linker DNA

Nucleosome consists of an octomer and a histone H1
between the linked regions of the chromosome

Chromatin and nucleosomes

Chromatin is a strand of nucleic acid and associated protein.

A nucleosome is a bead-like unit made of DNA wound around a complex of histone proteins.

When DNA is wrapped around several nucleosomes, the resulting structure looks like beads on a string.

Nucleosomes form the basic unit of coiling in DNA.

In turn, these nucleosomes form higher-order coils, as *supercoils*.

The level of supercoiling influences transcription, decreasing transcription levels for compacted DNA.

Human DNA is separated into 46 compact, supercoiled pieces (organized into 23 pairs) with nucleosomes and other proteins. These separate pieces of nucleic acid comprise the chromosomes.

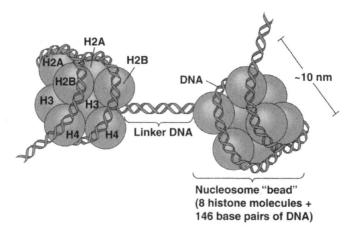

Single copy *vs.* repetitive DNA

Highly repetitive base sequences in DNA are between 5 and 300 nucleotide bases long and may be repeated up to 10,000 times. They are not translated into proteins. Highly repetitive base sequences constitute 5–45% of eukaryotic DNA. Single-copy genes (unique genes) are transcribed and translated to constitute a small proportion of eukaryotic DNA.

Centromeres hold sister chromatids during replication

A *centromere* is a heterochromatin (i.e., tightly coiled DNA) region on the chromosome at the center (metacentric) or near one of the ends (telocentric).

After replication, sister chromatids are attached at the centromere.

During mitosis, spindle fibers (comprised of tubulin) are attached to the centromere (via the kinetochore) and pull the sister chromatids apart during anaphase.

During anaphase of mitosis, the centromere splits, and the sister chromatids become chromosomes in the daughter cell during cell division.

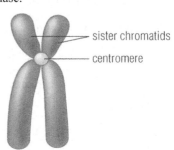

One chromosome with two sister chromatids attached at the centromere

Control of Gene Expression in Eukaryotes

Transcriptional control by DNA binding proteins

Transcriptional control in the nucleus determines which structural genes are transcribed and the rate of transcription. It includes the organization of chromatin and the protein transcription factors initiating transcription. Regulatory proteins include repressors and activators, and they influence the attachment of RNA polymerase to the promoter region on the DNA.

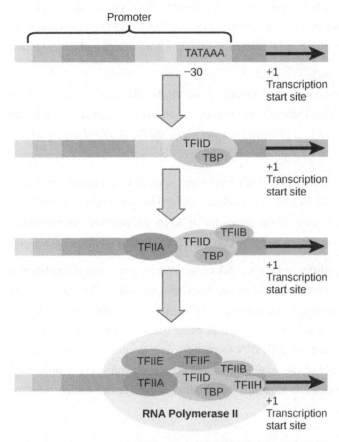

RNA transcription is influenced by transcription factor proteins that increase the affinity of the RNA polymerase and the rate of mRNA synthesis as enhancers or inhibitors

DNA binding proteins and transcription factors

Transcription factors are positively charged proteins with DNA-binding domains that allow them to bind to the promoter, enhancer, and silencer regions of DNA to regulate transcription. *Enhancers* increase transcription when bound, while *silencers* decrease it.

Transcription factors are influenced by intracellular or extracellular signals, accounting for the wide variation in gene expression in cell types. Pathways and types of signals exist to influence transcription factors, including the allosteric regulation of proteins and covalent modifications by kinases, phosphatases, and other enzymes. The DNA-binding domains themselves are varied in how they interact with the DNA double helix.

Common domains include helix-turn-helix (HTH), zinc finger, and basic region leucine zipper (bZIP).

Pre-initiation complex forms when transcription factors gather at the promoter region (segment of DNA where RNA polymerase binds) adjacent to a structural gene. The transcription factor complex leads to activation (or repression) of the gene. The complex attracts and binds RNA polymerase or promotes the separation of DNA strands. However, transcription may (or may not) begin at this point, depending on which transcription factors (activators or repressors) are bound.

While promoters are generally close to the affected gene in prokaryotes and eukaryotes, eukaryotic regulatory elements (i.e., enhancers and silencers) can be far from the promoter – even thousands of nucleotides away along the DNA strand that bends to stabilize the structure. This is not true for prokaryotic regulatory elements.

Since the enhancers and silencers must interact with the promoter to influence transcription, eukaryotic DNA can loop back on itself. The transcription factor bound to the enhancer or silencer can contact the promoter or RNA polymerase. Intermediate proteins between the transcription factors and RNA polymerase are often involved in the process.

Eukaryotes differ in that they lack certain special transcription regulation mechanisms in bacteria, such as the operon (except in rare cases) and attenuation. The *operon* (e.g., *lac* or *trp* operon) is a cluster of tandem genes in bacterial DNA under the control of a single promoter. Transcription of the operon results in several genes being transcribed simultaneously. *Attenuation* is a process where transcription and mRNA structure can influence ribosome translation. It is only possible in prokaryotes because transcription and translation can occur simultaneously. In eukaryotes, the two processes are separate; transcription occurs in the nucleus and translation occurs in the cytoplasm.

Gene amplification and duplication

Gene duplication (gene amplification or chromosomal duplication) is a mechanism by which genetic material is duplicated and serves as a molecular evolution source. There are many ways gene duplication occurs.

Ectopic recombination occurs during unequal crossing over between homologous chromosomes (during meiosis) due to the DNA sequence similarity at duplication breakpoints.

Replication slippage arises from an error in DNA replication; the DNA polymerase dissociates and re-attaches to the DNA at an incorrect position and mistakenly duplicates a section.

Aneuploidy (an abnormal number of chromosomes, often harmful) is another example of gene duplication, as is *polyploidy* (whole genome duplications), due to *nondisjunction*, the failure of sister chromatids (i.e., mitosis) or homologous chromosomes (i.e., meiosis) to separate properly during cell division.

Gene duplication is evolutionarily advantageous because it creates genetic redundancy.

A mutation in the second copy of a gene may not have harmful effects on the organism because the original gene can still function to encode functional protein products.

Since mutations of the second copy of a gene are not directly harmful, mutations accumulate rapidly (in the duplicated region) than usual. The second copy of the gene can develop a new function.

Therefore, gene duplication is believed to have played an essential role in evolution.

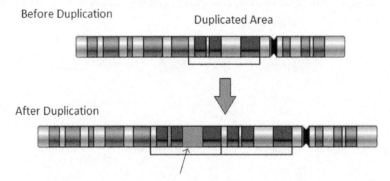

Point mutations are common in duplicated regions and accelerate the evolution of new proteins

Post-transcriptional control and mRNA splicing

Post-transcriptional control occurs in the nucleus after DNA has been transcribed and mRNA has formed. In this regulation, the RNA strands are processed before leaving the nucleus with certain variations.

Timing is one form of control. The speed at which mRNAs leave the nucleus affects the amount of gene product available per unit of time.

Various mRNA molecules differ in the rate they travel through the nuclear pores.

Additionally, mRNA must eventually be degraded, and the rate and timing of mRNA degradation, controlled by the cell, affect how much protein is translated. Modifications, such as adding a 5' cap and a 3' poly-A tail, affect control by protecting the mRNA from ribonuclease degradation.

Post-transcriptional control affects the sequences present in the RNA products.

Alternative splicing is the process by which introns are removed (cut from the transcript), and exons are ligated (rejoined) in different ways, forming mRNA products from the same initial hnRNA transcript.

The hypothalamus and thyroid gland contains the gene that encodes for the peptide hormone calcitonin, but the mRNA that leaves the nucleus, therefore the translated protein, is not the same in both types of cells.

Alternative splicing of the calcitonin gene occurs in the hypothalamus, leading to the production of a calcitonin gene-related peptide (CGRP). The thyroid gland produces regular calcitonin. Radioactive labeling experiments show different splicing in these strands.

Alternative splicing has been observed in cells that produce neurotransmitters, muscle regulatory proteins, and antibodies.

Additionally, experiments indicate that alternative splicing occurs at various development stages (i.e., embryogenic *vs.* adult cells).

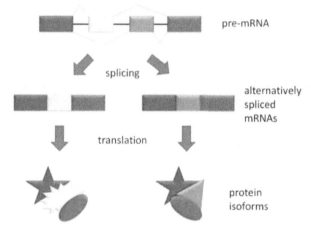

RNAs are subject to post-transcriptional control. For example, special modifications to nucleotides are made to control the structure of tRNA and rRNA.

Cancer

Cancer is a disorder that arises from mutations in the somatic cells and results from the failure of the control system that regulates cell division, which leads to uncontrolled growth. Cancer may develop in tissues and has terminology depending on the location and the way it develops.

Carcinomas are cancers in epithelial cells, *sarcomas* are cancers in muscle cells, and *lymphomas* are cancers involving white blood cells. The lungs, colon, and breasts are the organs commonly affected by cancer.

The incidence of cancer increases with age due to the accumulation of defective mutations (i.e., mutagen exposure or errors during DNA replication).

Oncogenes and tumor suppressor genes

Oncogenes are dominant cancer-producing genes encoded for irregular forms of cell surface receptors that bind growth factors, producing a continuous growth signal. Oncogenes cause cancer when they are activated. The products of many oncogenes are involved in increased cell division.

Before an oncogene is activated, it may be a harmless *proto-oncogene*. Researchers have identified several proto-oncogenes whose mutation to an oncogene cause increased growth and leads to tumor formation.

The *ras* (italicized, lowercase for the gene and capitalized for the corresponding protein) family of genes is the common group of oncogenes implicated in human cancers.

The alteration of one nucleotide pair converts a normal functioning *ras* proto-oncogene to an oncogene.

Tumor suppressor genes are recessive cancer-producing genes with mutated forms. Tumor suppressor genes protect cells from becoming cancerous by inhibiting tumor formation through cell division control.

Mutations in tumor suppressor genes alter the protective proteins encoded by these genes and disrupt their function, leading to cancer. A *tumor* is an abnormal replication of cells that form a tissue mass. If the cells remain localized, the tumor is *benign* (i.e., remains localized), but if the tumor invades the surrounding tissue because it undergoes metastasis, it is *malignant*.

Tumor-suppressor gene, *p53*, is frequently mutated in cancers compared to other known genes. The p53 protein acts as a transcription factor to turn on the expression of genes whose products are cell cycle inhibitors.

The p53 can stimulate *apoptosis* (i.e., programmed cell death), the ability of cells to self-destruct by autodigestion with endogenous enzymes. In apoptosis, the plasma membrane is kept intact, and the digested contents are not released; instead, phagocytic cells engulf the whole cell to eliminate these undesirable cells.

Cancer cells continue to grow and divide in situations where normal cells would not (lack contact inhibition); they fail to respond to cellular controls and signals that halt growth in normal cells. Cancer cells avoid the apoptosis (self-destruction) that normal cells undergo when extensive DNA damage occurs.

Cancer cells stimulate angiogenesis (the formation of new blood vessels) to nourish the cancer cell, and they are immortal (divide for generations after a normal cell). In contrast, normal cells die after some divisions.

Cancer cells can *metastasize* (relocate) and grows in another location.

Heterochromatin *vs*. euchromatin

DNA exists as euchromatin and heterochromatin within the cell.

Euchromatin is a looser conformation of DNA and histones than the tightly-condensed *heterochromatin*. Euchromatin appears lighter than the darker heterochromatin when viewed under an electron microscope.

DNA sequences in heterochromatin are generally repressed, while those in euchromatin are available and actively transcribed when the RNA polymerase binds to the single-stranded DNA.

Much of the satellite DNA (large, tandem repeats of noncoding DNA) appears in heterochromatin.

Euchromatin is transcribed while heterochromatin is not transcribed

When DNA is transcribed, activators known as remodeling proteins can push aside the histone portion of the chromatin, allowing transcription to begin.

During interphase (G_1, S, and G_2 phase), chromatin exists as either of the two types, but it condenses to supercoiled heterochromatin during mitosis.

Chromatin remodeling

The form of compactness that the DNA adopts depends on the cell's cellular needs and is regulated by covalent *histone modifications* by specific enzymes.

Examples of modifications are *histone methylation*, causing tighter packing that prevents transcription.

Histone acetylation uncoils DNA and promotes transcription.

There are other types of histone modifications, such as ubiquitination and phosphorylation.

As an active area of investigation, the *histone code hypothesis* states that DNA transcription is partly regulated by these histone modifications, especially on the unstructured ends of histones.

Chromatin remodeling complexes are another mechanism for regulating chromatin structure. These protein complexes are ATP-dependent and thus have a common ATPase domain.

ATP hydrolysis gives these domains the energy to reposition nucleosomes and move histones, creating uncoiled DNA regions available for transcription.

DNA methylation regulates gene expression

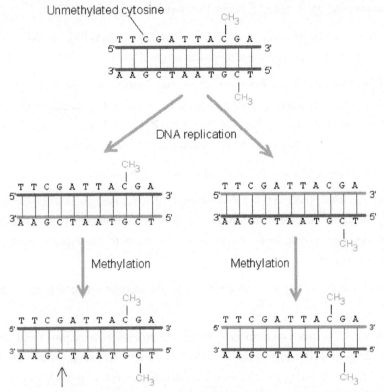

Modifications such as methylation facilitate proper DNA repair

DNA methylation, which reduces the transcription rate, is another method that the cell uses to regulate gene expression. DNA methyltransferase enzymes add a methyl ($-CH_3$) group to the cytosine bases of DNA, converting them to 5-methylcytosine.

The methylated cytosine residues are usually adjacent to guanine, which results in methylated cytosines diagonal from each other.

DNA methylation patterns are heritable to daughter cells, as it is passed on during cell division.

Epigenetics studies potential transcriptional changes (such as DNA methylation and histone modification) that do not involve DNA sequence changes.

Non-coding RNA for regulatory control

Non-coding RNA (ncRNA) is functional RNA not translated into proteins. They have an essential role in many cellular processes, including RNA splicing, DNA replication, and the regulation of gene expression.

ncRNA can participate in histone modification, DNA methylation, and heterochromatin formation.

The majority of ncRNA are *long ncRNA* (over 200 nucleotides) that form a complex with chromatin-modifying proteins and function in chromatin remodeling.

There are three classes of *short ncRNA* (less than 30 nucleotides), including microRNA (miRNA), short interfering RNAs, and piwi-interacting RNA.

microRNAs (miRNA) are folded RNA molecules with hairpin loops that bind to target mRNA sequences through complementary base pairing. miRNA can induce degradation of the mRNA by shortening its poly-A tail, which destabilizes the mRNA, or they can cleave the mRNA into pieces. This silences the mRNA and prevents translation from occurring.

A single miRNA molecule can target and repress several mRNAs.

Short interfering RNAs (siRNAs) are double-stranded RNA molecules often created through catalysis by the Dicer enzyme, which produces siRNAs from longer double-stranded RNAs. siRNAs function similarly to miRNAs, as they interfere with the expression of genes with complementary sequences.

siRNA degrades mRNA, blocks translation, induces heterochromatin formation, and blocks transcription.

Piwi-interacting RNAs (piRNA) form RNA-protein complexes with the piwi family of proteins, and they are the largest class of short ncRNA in animal cells. They suppress transposon activity in germline cells by forming an *RNA-induced silencing complex*. piRNAs do not have any known secondary structure motifs.

Recombinant DNA and Biotechnology

Genetic engineering

Recombinant DNA refers to a genetic material that has been artificially "recombined" from disparate sources. The recombination of these DNA segments can occur through viral transduction, bacterial conjugation, transposons, or artificial recombinant DNA technology.

Crossing over during meiosis prophase I produce recombinant chromosomes.

Recombinant DNA plays a significant role in contemporary society. For example, genetically modified crops and many meat sources rely on recombinant DNA technologies.

Additionally, several important pharmaceuticals are assembled using recombination technologies. As the techniques available to manipulate genetic material become sophisticated, recombinant technologies become a larger part of everyday life.

Gene cloning

A *clone* is a genetically identical organism (or a group of genetically identical cells) derived from a single parental cell.

Gene cloning refers to the production of identical copies of the same gene.

When a gene is cloned, the first step is to extract and purify the DNA from the organism of interest.

The gene of interest is introduced into the nucleotide sequence of another organism.

Restriction enzymes (i.e., extracted from bacterial cells) cut double-stranded DNA at specific nucleotide sequences to generate DNA fragments (some with sticky ends).

These fragments are incorporated into commercially available bacterial vector plasmids (circular pieces of DNA) that are cut by the same restriction enzymes to hybridize the sticky ends.

The plasmid is the vector.

The foreign gene is sealed into the vector DNA by the enzyme DNA ligase, and the plasmids are introduced into bacteria by transformation.

Before this, the bacteria must be "made competent" to take up the plasmid; this is done through *electroporation*, where an electric field increases the cell membrane's permeability, or *heat shock*, which increases the fluidity of the membrane, allowing plasmids to pass through the membrane more easily.

Subcloning moves a gene of interest from a parent (i.e., source) vector to a target vector.

This multi-step process is shown in the following diagram.

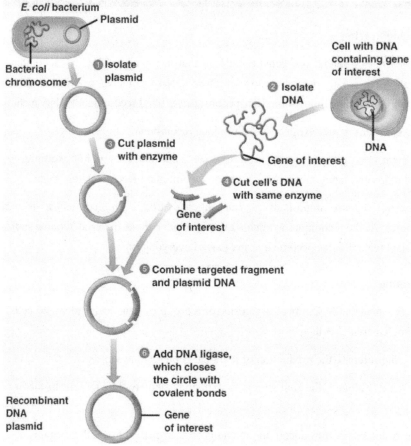

Subcloning by constructing a plasmid with the "gene of interest" to synthesize proteins

Transformation

Transformation is the update of DNA by bacterial cells.

A screening method, such as incorporating an antibiotic-resistant gene on the plasmid and cultivation on an antibiotic-containing medium, inhibits the growth of the colonies without the recombinant DNA.

The transformed bacteria are allowed to grow at optimum conditions, thus creating copies (i.e., cloning) of the gene of interest. See diagram below.

If a eukaryotic gene is to be expressed in a bacterium, it must be accompanied by the regulatory regions unique to bacteria.

The eukaryotic gene cannot contain introns because bacteria do not have the cellular mechanisms necessary to remove introns and ligate the remaining exons.

If a prokaryotic gene is to be cloned into a mammalian cell, a poly-A tail must be added to the mRNA.

The protein is expressed within the recombinant cells to study the gene's functionality.

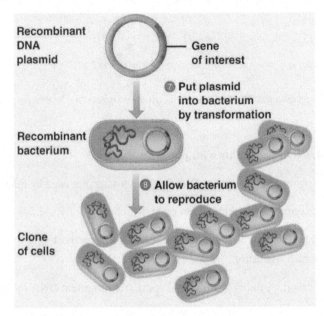

Subcloning is used to move a gene of interest from a parent vector (i.e., source vector) to a destination vector (i.e., target vector). This allows the protein to be expressed within the recombinant cells for the gene's functionality to be further studied.

Restriction enzymes in molecular biology

A *restriction enzyme* (restriction endonuclease) is an enzyme that can recognize and cut double-stranded DNA at specific nucleotide sequences.

Bacteria and archaea naturally produce them to defend the cell (analogous to a primitive immune system) against viruses by destroying viral DNA and restricting the growth of viruses: "restriction" enzymes.

The restriction enzymes synthesized by a strain of bacteria do not recognize "self" and therefore do not cut the endogenous DNA. Therefore, a bacterium is unaffected by its restriction enzymes.

Restriction enzymes are usually named for the species from which they were isolated; for example, *Bam*HI was isolated from *Bacillus amyloliquefaciens* strain H, and *Eco*RI was isolated from *E. coli* strain RY13.

Recombinant DNA technology uses restriction enzymes as molecular scissors, cleaving DNA pieces at specific nucleotide palindrome sequences.

Palindrome sequences read the same from 5' → 3' of one strand and 5' → 3' of the other strand.

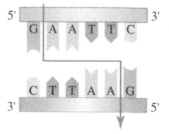

The restriction enzyme cuts DNA along the sequence shown by the arrow to generate sticky ends

Hybridizing restriction fragments with plasmids

Restriction fragments are the resulting DNA fragments after cleavage by restriction enzymes.

Some restriction enzymes cut to make *blunt ends*, which cannot hybridize.

Other restriction enzymes cut at staggered locations to make short single-stranded segments with *sticky ends*, which hybridize.

Hybridization anneals (i.e., joins) plasmid and restriction fragment DNA by forming hydrogen bonds.

The "sticky ends" allow for directional insertion of foreign DNA into vector DNA (catalyzed by DNA ligase, creating phosphodiester bonds between DNA pieces).

An example of a blunt end, where N represents one of the four unspecified nucleotides:

```
5'   NNNNNNNATT          AATNNNNNNNNNN  3'
3'   NNNNNNNTAA          TTANNNNNNNNNN5'
```

An example of a sticky end:

```
5'   NNNNNNNNNNNNNNNNG          AATTCNNNNNNNNNNN  3'
3'   NNNNNNNTTAA          CNNNNNNNNNNNNNNNNNNNNN5'
```

The nucleotides at the cut's location must be the nucleotides specified as the target sequence recognized and cut by a restriction enzyme.

DNA libraries screen for genes

After DNA is extracted from an organism, a *DNA library* (gene library) is constructed to organize an organism's DNA.

A DNA library represents, stores, and propagates a collection of genes using live populations of microorganisms; populations contain a different restriction fragment inserted into a cloning vector.

There are several types of DNA libraries.

A *genomic library* contains a set of nucleotide clones representing the entire genome of an organism.

The number of clones in a genomic library can vary, depending on the size of the genome of that organism and the size of the DNA fragment that is inserted into the cloning vector used in the library.

Genomic libraries are useful for studying the function of regulatory sequences, introns, untranscribed regions of DNA and for studying genetic mutations that may occur in disease or cancer tissues.

A *cDNA library* represents the genes from an organism actively expressed.

The cDNA (complementary DNA) is reverse transcribed from expressed mRNA isolated from the cell. This is usually less than 1% of the genome in an organism.

cDNA libraries are useful for studying the mRNAs expressed in specific cells or tissues and detecting alternative splicing of genes.

A *randomized mutant library* is created by the *de novo* synthesis of a gene.

While the DNA is synthesized in the laboratory, alternative nucleotides are added into the sequence at various positions, resulting in a mix of DNA molecule variants of the original gene.

These variants are cloned into vectors, creating the library.

Randomized mutant libraries are used to screen for proteins with favorable properties, such as improved binding affinity, enzyme activity, or stability.

cDNA for expressing desired proteins

cDNA can be synthesized by the enzyme *reverse transcriptase*, which synthesizes a DNA copy of processed mRNA.

Reverse transcriptase is generally associated with *retroviruses*, which use this enzyme to reverse-transcribe their RNA genome into DNA when infecting a host (e.g., HIV).

Reverse transcriptase can naturally be in viruses, prokaryotes, and eukaryotes. This enzyme is utilized for the mRNA-template synthesis of cDNA, which is necessary for biotechnology for several recombinant techniques.

As of 2021, there are six known retroviruses (i.e., viruses using reverse transcriptase).

cDNA does not contain introns. Bacteria are transfected with the cDNA of human genes to produce large quantities of human proteins.

For example, mRNA encoding for insulin is extracted from a human pancreatic cell that produces insulin. cDNA copies are made from this mRNA by using reverse transcriptase.

A selected plasmid is cut using the same restriction enzymes.

The plasmid and the gene are combined, and the DNA (gene and plasmid) fragments hybridize.

Bacterial host cells are transformed with recombinant plasmids with the integrated human insulin gene.

The bacteria cell translates the insulin protein.

It must be collected and purified. cDNA, rather than genomic DNA, must be used because bacterial DNA does not have the cellular proteins to undergo splicing (i.e., a mechanism to excise introns and ligate exons).

DNA denaturation, reannealing and hybridization

Double-stranded DNA is reversibly *denatured* into single-stranded DNA when subjected to heat or extreme pH, causing the hydrogen bonds linking A−T and C−G complementary nitrogenous bases to disassociate.

Annealing is the opposite process, where subsequent cooling, or return to physiological pH in the presence of salt, the hydrogen bonds to re-associate, forming double-stranded DNA from single-stranded DNA.

During *hybridization*, which is an important part of many biotechnology techniques, complementary base pairs anneal by hydrogen bonding.

Expressing cloned genes to harvest therapeutic proteins

Genes are cloned into an expression vector (i.e., plasmid or a virus) and are inserted into a host (usually bacteria, but may be yeast, fungi, or eukaryotes).

Expression of that gene is when the host cells with the donor DNA produce protein from the gene of interest (recombinant) as they undergo normal protein synthesis.

When cloned genes are expressed in industrial settings, the goal is to make a large quantity of the protein, so the expression is at an extremely high level as *overexpression*.

The *recombinant protein* is the targeted protein that is subsequently isolated and purified.

Eukaryotic host cell lines (host cells) are used to produce proteins that require significant post-translational modifications or RNA splicing because prokaryotic cells lack the necessary machinery for these processes.

However, using bacteria for protein expression has a distinct advantage because bacterial cells allow for large-scale protein production (due to short replication times for bacterial cell growth).

Because of the ease of growth, low cost to maintain the cells, and short replication cycles, *E. coli* is among the frequently used hosts for expressing cloned genes.

Notes for active learning

Targeted Nucleotide Amplification

Polymerase chain reaction (PCR) amplifies target DNA

Polymerase chain reaction (PCR) was developed in 1983 by Kary Mullis.

PCR exponentially generates millions of copies of a piece of DNA in a test tube.

PCR is specific, so the targeted DNA sequence is less than one part in a million of the DNA sample.

A single gene can be amplified.

There are several components necessary for PCR.

One component is the DNA template (e.g., forensic sample) containing the DNA region to be amplified.

Additionally, two primers (short strands of DNA, usually between 14 and 20 nucleotides) complementary to the 3' ends of the coding and template strand of the DNA target are needed ("forward" and "reverse" primer, respectively).

The enzyme *DNA polymerase* replicates the DNA and requires nucleotide primers to initiate synthesis.

PCR uses high temperatures, so the DNA polymerase enzyme must withstand heat without denaturing.

Taq polymerase from *Thermus aquaticus* (bacterium lives in hot thermal springs) is frequently used.

PCR components include deoxynucleoside triphosphates (dNTP – dATP, dGTP, dCTP, and dTTP); the four "building blocks" used by DNA polymerase while synthesizing a complementary strand of DNA.

These dNTPs lose two phosphate groups when incorporated into the growing strand and become adenine, guanine, cytosine, and thymine.

PCR uses a buffer solution containing cations (often Mg^{2+}), required to stabilize the DNA polymerase as it binds to the complementary strand of the negatively charged DNA sample to be amplified.

PCR uses three steps to amplify DNA

PCR involves three steps. First is denaturation, where heat is applied (about 94 °C) to separate the double-stranded DNA template.

Annealing is when the mixture is cooled (about 54 °C) for primers to hybridize (anneal) to the now single-stranded DNA template.

Excessive primers are added to outcompete in re-annealing of the parent DNA strands that were separated during the initial heating.

The last step is elongation (about 72 °C), where heat-stable DNA polymerase extends the primers along the respective target DNA strands.

20 to 30 rounds of PCR are performed to create large quantities of amplified DNA fragments.

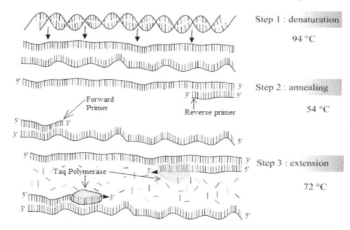

Polymerase Chain Reaction: temperatures depend on DNA sample and primers

PCR amplification for sample analysis

PCR amplification and subsequent DNA analysis are often used to detect viral infections, genetic disorders, and cancer.

It determines the nucleotide sequence of genes (e.g., Human Genome Project, forensics, identification).

PCR can use DNA from many sources, including blood, semen, and various tissues, so it is useful in forensics when a small amount of DNA is available.

If a DNA fragment undergoes 30 PCR cycles, the result is $2^{30} \approx 1.02 \times 10^9$ copies of the DNA fragment.

A limitation of PCR amplification is fidelity.

The heat-resistant bacterial DNA *Taq* polymerase, unlike eukaryotic polymerases, does not perform "proofreading" during replication.

Therefore, mistakes are expected at about one mutation per million nucleotides replicated during mismatching between the newly synthesized and parental strand.

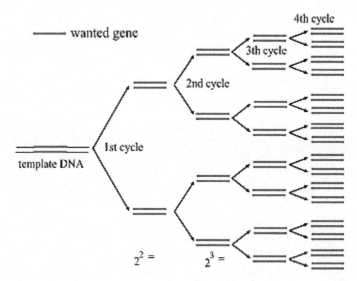

Notes for active learning

Molecular Biology Techniques Analyze DNA, RNA and Proteins

Gel electrophoresis to resolve fragments

In *gel electrophoresis*, macromolecules such as DNA, RNA, and proteins are separated (resolved) by size or charge. The macromolecules move through an agarose or polyacrylamide gel due to an applied electric field consisting of a negative charge and a positive charge at the other end.

DNA is negatively charged, so it moves away from a negative cathode toward a positive anode. Electrophoresis uses an electrolytic cell, so the charge of the cathode is negative, and the anode is positive. Based on resistance within the gel, larger DNA fragments migrate less than shorter fragments.

During gel electrophoresis, the DNA molecules are resolved according to size, resulting in a visible pattern of bands. The same separation based upon size is observed for RNA, proteins, or macromolecules.

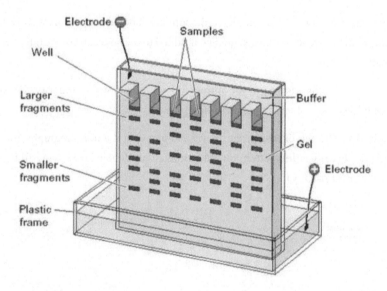

A *molecular weight ruler*, or *DNA ladder*, containing a mixture of DNA fragments of known sizes is run on the gel along with the DNA fragments. The unknown sizes of the resolved fragments are measured by comparing them to the known sizes of the ladder (i.e., reference values) once electrophoresis is complete.

Proteins are separated by polyacrylamide gel electrophoresis (PAGE). Before electrophoresis, they are denatured (i.e., unfolded) with sodium dodecyl sulfate (SDS), which imparts a distribution of negative charge per unit mass on the proteins. The procedure is referred to as SDS-PAGE.

The migration of proteins in SDS-PAGE (similar to DNA) is inversely proportional to the macromolecules' molecular weight (i.e., smaller molecules move further than larger molecules due to resistance).

Southern blotting targets DNA fragments

Southern blotting identifies target DNA fragments in a large sample of DNA.

The DNA is cut into fragments by restriction enzymes, and fragments are resolved (i.e., separated) by gel electrophoresis.

The double-stranded DNA is denatured in an alkaline environment, separating the DNA into single strands for later hybridization.

The single-stranded DNA is transferred to a nitrocellulose membrane by applying pressure, and capillary action transfers the DNA from the gel to the membrane.

The membrane is baked (i.e., fixed) at high temperatures so that the DNA becomes permanently attached.

The hybridization probe (a single radioactively-labeled or fluorescently-labeled DNA fragment) with the predetermined sequence is added to the solution containing the nitrocellulose membrane.

This labeled probe hybridizes to the nitrocellulose membrane to identify the location of the sequence of DNA (resolved by gel electrophoresis).

After hybridization, the excess probe is washed away, and autoradiography (or fluorescence) visualizes the hybridization pattern on the radioactively-labeled (via x-ray film) or fluorescent sample (via spectroscopy).

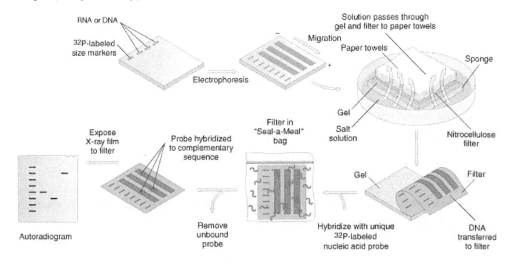

Southern blot method where gel electrophoresis and the fragment resolves DNA is located by hybridization of the labeled probe with a complementary sequence to the target gene

Northern and Western blotting for RNA and proteins

Northern blotting is similar to Southern blotting but uses RNA instead of DNA.

Western blotting is the equivalent technique used for proteins, where antibodies bind to the protein of interest and mark it for visualization.

Use the mnemonic SNoW DRoP and match the letters.

S -   Southern - DNA   - D

N -   Northern - RNA   - R

o -   - o

W - Western - Protein   - P

DNA sequencing to determine the gene structure

DNA sequencing determines the precise nucleotide sequence in a DNA molecule.

The most popular method for DNA sequencing is the *dideoxy method*, known as the *chain termination method* or "Sanger sequencing."

It was created by Fredrick Sanger, awarded the 1980 Nobel Prize in chemistry for this discovery.

DNA is synthesized from four deoxynucleotide triphosphates (dNTPs), each contains a 3' OH group.

The Sanger sequencing method uses fluorescently-tagged synthetic dideoxynucleotides (ddNTP) that lack the 3'−OH group.

When a dideoxynucleotide is randomly added to a growing DNA strand, the strand cannot be elongated because there is no 3'−OH for the next nucleotide to attach.

The ddNTPs are present in limited quantities. A dNTP may add depending on probability, allowing the growing DNA strand to continue elongation, or a ddNTP may get added, terminating the strand.

This results in various DNA strands of various lengths, separated by gel electrophoresis.

An instrument identifies the fluorescent ddNTPs, and since the four ddNTPs are labeled a unique color, the DNA sequence are read by an automatic scanner.

Sanger sequencing works well for DNA fragments of up to 900 nucleotides.

Shotgun sequencing for genome structure

For longer pieces of DNA (e.g., entire genomes), *shotgun sequencing* is used.

In shotgun sequencing, a long piece of DNA is randomly cut into smaller fragments, cloned into vectors, and sequenced individually by the dideoxy method.

A computer analyzes the sequences to search for overlapping sequences and reassembled them into the proper order. This yields the full sequence of the original piece of DNA.

Pairwise-end sequencing is a variety of shotgun sequencing that analyzes the ends of DNA fragments for overlap as an ideal method for longer genomes.

Several high-throughput sequencing methods do not use Sanger sequencing; they are *next-generation sequencing* and have been developed to meet the high demand for low-cost sequencing (e.g., ancestry analysis).

These sequencing techniques utilize parallel processing and generate millions of sequences concurrently.

Analyzing Gene Expression from RNA Levels

mRNA levels for quantifying gene expression

Different cells in the body express various combinations of genes that encode for distinct products.

In addition to quantifying gene expression, analyzing the location of expression (cell type or stages of development) are useful. There are methods to quantify the level at which genes are expressed, and the information obtained from these gene expression analysis methods is useful.

For example, the expression levels of an oncogene (growth factor promoting gene) can determine a person's susceptibility to cancer.

Genes are transcribed into mRNA and then translated into proteins, so mRNA and protein are gene products. Depending on the study's intent, expression levels of mRNA or proteins are quantified.

One approach for measuring mRNA levels is the Northern blot, mentioned earlier.

Another approach is using *reverse transcriptase PCR* (RT-PCR). In RT-PCR, a primer anneals to a specific mRNA strand, and the enzyme reverse transcriptase synthesizes a cDNA copy of the mRNA.

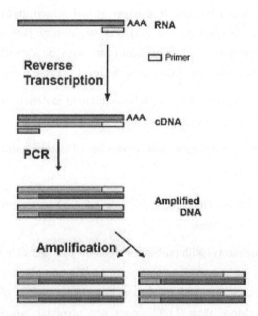

*RT-PCR identifies expressed genes from mRNA
containing a poly-A tail as the original template*

Standard PCR protocol replicates this cDNA, followed by gel electrophoresis to separate the resulting DNA fragments. If the DNA fragment with the suspected molecular weight appears on the gel, the mRNA sequence of interest is present in the sample, and it may be concluded that the gene of interest is being expressed.

Gel electrophoresis of the RT-PCR product is performed along with standardized samples of known mRNA amounts. By comparison, the expression level is calculated from how much mRNA is expressed by the gene.

DNA microarrays for gene expression

DNA microarrays evaluate gene expression using small glass chips containing many DNA fragments to probe for specific genes. DNA microarrays allow for the simultaneous analysis of thousands of gene products.

To use a DNA microarray, mRNA must be extracted from the cells being studied and reverse transcribed (RT-PCR) into cDNA labeled with a fluorescent probe.

The cDNA is combined with the microarray so it can base pair with the attached DNA fragments. An automated microscope scans the DNA microarray to determine which DNA fragments have bound. This analysis provides a complete and precise profile of gene expression.

For protein quantification, a Western blot is performed, which gives information about the protein's size (i.e., its location on the gel) and its identity (antibody bound). Although modifications to the protein (e.g., ubiquitination) can easily be identified because this method is sensitive to protein size changes, quantifying the level of protein expression is not accurate.

Quantitative mass spectrometry (MS) is a reliable method to determine the amount of protein expressed. In quantitative MS, isotopic tags distinguish the proteins.

When viewing the mass spectrum, the peak intensities of isotope pairs indicate the abundance of corresponding proteins.

DNA microarrays determine changes in the level of gene expression. This can lead to an evaluation of the genes' functions.

For example, DNA microarrays with probes for all 6,000 yeast genes have been used to monitor gene expression as the yeast is made to shift from growing on glucose to growing on ethanol. About 1,000 genes increase in activity during this change, while about 1,000 other genes decrease in activity. More than 2,000 genes are involved when yeast switches from metabolizing glucose to metabolizing ethanol.

Determining gene function

One of the direct methods to determine a gene's function is to study mutant organisms with changes in their nucleotide sequence that disrupt the gene.

Spontaneous mutants may be in populations, but it is more efficient to generate mutations with DNA-damaging mutagens.

Besides exposing the organism to mutagens, *insertional mutagenesis* is another method to create interruptions in the genetic code by inserting exogenous DNA into the genome.

Although humans are not used in these processes for ethical reasons, model organisms such as Drosophila flies, zebrafish, and yeast are used.

After a collection of mutants has been created, a *genetic screen* determines the altered phenotypes.

Suppose the phenotype of interest is a metabolic deficiency (e.g., organism that cannot grow without a specific nutrient). The genetic screen is simple to perform, but screening for subtle phenotypes is challenging. The next step is to identify the gene causing the altered phenotype.

If insertional mutagenesis was used, the DNA fragments containing the insertion could be amplified via PCR, sequenced (e.g., Sanger sequencing), and searched in a DNA database to find homologous genes.

However, if mutagens were used, the process of locating and identifying the gene is laborious.

Chromosomal location of genes

One method to determine the gene's chromosomal location is by estimating the distance between genetic loci by calculating the recombination frequency, a technique of *linkage analysis*.

Once the gene is located, it is searched on a database to find homologous genes and ascertain function.

In 2007, the Nobel prize was awarded for creating a *knockout organism*, where the gene of interest was "knocked out" (i.e., inactivated) in a mouse.

Knockout organisms are often made by inserting DNA with the altered gene into target vectors, transformed into embryonic stem cells, and inserted into early embryos of the organism.

By studying the phenotype of the resulting organism and comparing it to the wild type (i.e., the most common phenotype in nature), the knock-out gene's function is determined.

Mutant libraries are created as collections of organisms of a species that have genes systematically deleted. These are extremely valuable tools for studying the roles of various genes.

93

In addition to knockouts, mutants are generated that overexpress a gene or express it at the wrong time or in the wrong tissue. These studies provide essential information about a gene's function.

Application of Biotechnology

Stem cells in human therapy

Stem cells are not fully differentiated (i.e., morphologically or biochemically distinct) and renew themselves through cell division and divide and differentiate into specialized cell types.

For example, a single stem cell may differentiate into a blood cell, liver cell, or kidney cell. In many tissues, *somatic stem cells* (adult stem cells) function as an internal repair system and can replace damaged cells or tissues by differentiating into tissue-specific cells. Since different types of cells in the adult organism originate from a single zygote, *embryonic stem cells* are necessary for embryonic development.

Stem cell therapy uses stem cells to treat diseases. A bone marrow transplant is the common therapeutic use of stem cells. Stem cells in the bone marrow give rise to red blood cells, white blood cells, and platelets. When a patient has cancer and is given high doses of chemotherapy, it targets the intended cancer cells.

However, chemotherapy destroys noncancerous cells in the bone marrow, which prevents the patient from producing blood cells. To avoid this, before the patient is treated with chemotherapy, she can undergo a bone marrow harvest where stem cells are removed from the bone marrow by using a needle inserted into the pelvis (hip bone).

Alternatively, if the patient's stem cells cannot be used, they are harvested from a matching donor.

After chemotherapy, the patient undergoes a bone marrow transplant in which the stem cells are transplanted into the patient through a drip, usually via a vein in the chest or the arm.

These transplanted stem cells migrate to the bone marrow and produce healthy blood cells.

Therefore, the therapeutic use of stem cells in bone marrow transplants allows cancer patients to undergo high-dose chemotherapy treatment. Without this therapeutic use of stem cells, patients would be able to take low doses of chemotherapy to avoid destroying bone marrow cells needed for replenishing blood cells. Their chances of recovering from cancer are reduced.

Several ongoing studies are testing the use of stem cells for the regeneration of brain tissue, heart tissue, and other tissue to treat diseases such as Alzheimer's, diabetes, heart disease, and Crohn's disease.

Different stem cells are being studied, including adult stem cells, amniotic stem cells (from the fluid of the amniotic sac where the fetus develops), induced pluripotent stem cells (created by reprogramming adult cells), and embryonic stem cells.

Embryonic stem cells are taken from the inner cell mass of a blastocyst, a structure formed in the early stages of embryo development.

Disadvantages of stem cell therapy

If stem cells are harvested from a donor with a different major histocompatibility complex (MHC), the patient's immune system will target the stem cells (i.e., antibodies mount an immune response) and reject them. Therefore, a well-matching donor must be identified for stem cell transplantation to be effective.

Additionally, the stem cells' ability to differentiate into a specific cell type may pose a problem if they do not differentiate into the cell type needed for treatment.

Stem cells pose the risk of forming tumors (uncontrolled cell growth).

Practical applications of DNA technology

Recombinant DNA technologies have many practical applications, especially in medicine and in the development of pharmaceuticals. For example, medical products (e.g., insulin) are expressed in *E. coli* cells. Large quantities of the protein are cultured and used to treat diseases (e.g., diabetes, cancer, and viral infections).

Recombinant DNA is utilized to create vaccines. The outside protein shell of an infectious virus is combined with a harmless host so that the surface proteins activate the patient's immune system but are not infected with the virus.

Gene therapy involves introducing healthy patient genes to compensate for defective ones, helping to treat genetic diseases and other illnesses.

Gene therapy is classified into *ex vivo* (cells are modified outside the body) and *in vivo* (cells are modified inside the body). Gene therapy is still being developed for use in the clinic.

Treatment of adenosine deaminase (ADA) deficiency may involve manipulating stem cells for *ex vivo* gene therapy.

ADA deficiency is a severe combined immunodeficiency (SCID), in which the lack of functional ADA enzyme causes inhibition of DNA synthesis as well as toxicity to immune cells, leading to immunodeficiency.

In this treatment, bone marrow stem cells are removed, infected with a retrovirus that carries a normal gene for the ADA enzyme, and returned to the patient.

Because the genes are replaced in the stem cells, the genes are spread into many cells during cell division, leading to greater production of the functional enzyme. Patients have shown significant improvement.

In *ex vivo* gene therapy for familial hypercholesterolemia, a condition where liver cells lack a receptor for removing cholesterol from the blood is treated. High cholesterol leads to fatal heart attacks at a young age.

During treatment, a small portion of the liver is surgically removed and infected with a retrovirus with a normal gene for the receptor. The cells infected with the gene are reintroduced into the patient, leading to lowered cholesterol levels in the patients receiving this treatment.

Potential *in vivo* gene therapy treatment for cancer involves making cancer cells vulnerable to chemotherapy and making normal cells resistant.

Injecting a retrovirus containing a normal *TP53* gene that promotes apoptosis of cells into tumors may inhibit their growth.

In another *in vivo* gene therapy, a gene for a vascular endothelial growth factor (VEGF) can be injected alone (or within a virus) into the heart to stimulate branching of coronary blood vessels (i.e., angiogenesis), helping to treat heart disease.

Medical applications from The Human Genome Project

To properly utilize gene therapy treatments, it is important to understand the genetic basis of disease.

The Human Genome Project, launched in the 1980s by the National Institutes of Health (NIH, Bethesda, MD) and assisted by other research teams such as Craig Venter, was a major help with these efforts.

The Human Genome Project aimed to map the nucleotide base pair sequences along the 23 human chromosomes. It took 15 years to learn the sequence of the three billion base pairs along the length of human chromosomes.

The cost to sequence a genome of the human (or a person) has decreased from $2.7 billion to approximately $1,000, making sequencing for medical applications more affordable through advances in technology.

The Human Genome Project found few differences between the sequence of bases within humans and many other organisms with known DNA sequences.

Since complex organisms (e.g., humans) share such a large number of genes with simpler organisms, the uniqueness of a complex organism may be due to the regulation of these genes. For example, about 97% of human DNA does not encode for protein product and includes noncoding DNA, regulatory sequences, introns, and untranscribed repetitive sequences.

Tandem repeats (*satellite DNA*) are abnormally long stretches of contiguous repetitive sequences within an affected gene and cause disease in some instances (e.g., Huntington's disease). The Human Genome Project helped to elucidate the identity and relative amounts of different types of DNA sequences.

Additionally, the Human Genome Project studied mitochondrial DNA sequences, which provided information on the origins, evolution, and migration of ancestral humans.

With the sequencing of the complete human genome, it is now easier to study how genes influence human development and identify many genetic diseases.

Sequencing of the human genome allows for new pharmaceuticals based on DNA sequences of genes or the structure of proteins encoded by these genes.

Forensics and paternity tests

Information about the human genome is useful in *forensic science,* analyzing physical evidence by crime investigators and presented in court during a trial.

The genome of humans differs roughly once per 1,000 nucleotides; these differences are *single nucleotide polymorphisms* (SNPs).

Short tandem repeats (STR) have 2 to 5 nucleotides, which differ except for identical twins.

Restriction fragment length polymorphisms (RFLPs) are the differences in fragment lengths after restriction enzymes cut the DNA sequences from different samples.

The genetic sequences that give rise to RFLPs are inherited in a Mendelian fashion.

Forensic scientists use RFLP analysis to compare the DNA at the crime scene (e.g., in traces of blood or semen) with the suspect's DNA.

For a paternity test, the child's DNA is compared with that of the putative father.

These are *DNA fingerprinting* examples, using DNA to identify individuals since no two individuals share identical genomes.

DNA fingerprinting and PCR can identify deceased individuals from skeletal remains.

Applications of genetic engineering

Genetic engineering is the manipulation of the genome of an organism.

An important aspect of genetic engineering is the ability to move a gene from one organism to another.

This process first involves splicing out a gene of interest by a restriction enzyme.

This gene is placed into another organism by cutting the target chromosome and sealing the new sequence with DNA ligase.

The target organism now has a gene sequence for polypeptide production.

Transgenic organisms, or organisms with a foreign gene that has been inserted, are genetically engineered to produce specific protein products.

Some products include enzymes used in chemical synthesis for substances that may otherwise be expensive to produce.

For example, phenylalanine, used in aspartame sweeteners, is produced by transgenic bacteria.

Transgenic bacteria have been used to protect the health of plants from environmental issues.

Ice-minus bacteria have been created by removing genes encoding a specific protein on the outer cell wall of *Pseudomonas syringae* that facilitates ice formation.

The introduction of this genetically modified bacteria protects vegetative plant parts from frost damage.

Root-colonizing bacteria with inserted insect toxin genes protect corn roots from damage by insects.

Cleanup of various substances can utilize genetic engineering.

For example, transgenic bacteria can be optimized for oil degradation or formed into a bio-filter to reduce the number of chemical pollutants flowing into the air.

Some bacteria remove sulfur from coal before it is burned to clean up toxic dumps.

These bacteria are given "suicide genes" that cause them to die after doing their job.

Bacteria can be engineered to process minerals. Genetically engineered "bio-leaching" bacteria extract copper, uranium, and gold from low-grade ore.

Many major mining companies already use bacteria to obtain various metals.

In addition to bacteria, transgenic plants and animals can be engineered.

Protoplasts are plant cells with their cell wall removed. An electric current makes tiny holes in the plasma membrane through which genetic material enters the cell. The protoplasts develop into mature plants. Foreign genes now give cotton, corn, and potato strains to produce an insect toxin. Crops are made resistant to certain herbicides so that the crop plants are sprayed with the herbicide and not be affected by it.

Plants are engineered to produce human proteins (e.g., hormones, clotting factors, antibodies) in seeds.

Antibodies made by corn can deliver radioisotopes to tumor cells, and a soybean-engineered antibody can treat genital herpes. Mouse-eared cress has been engineered to produce biodegradable plastic in cell granules.

Cloning organisms

The creation of transgenic animals requires methods to insert genes into animals' eggs.

Foreign genes can be manually microinjected into the eggs, or a vortex mixing is used.

Vortex (mixing) involves placing the eggs in an agitator with DNA and silicon-carbide needles that make tiny holes through which the DNA can enter the egg.

Many types of animal eggs have been injected with bovine growth hormone (bGH) to produce larger fish, cows, pigs, rabbits, and sheep using this technique.

It may be possible to use genetically engineered pigs to serve as a source of organs for human transplant.

Gene pharming uses transgenic farm animals to produce pharmaceuticals; the product is obtainable from the milk of females.

One example is the transfer of the gene for factor IX, a blood clotting factor, from humans into sheep so that this factor is produced in the sheep's milk.

Clones are cells identical to the parent and arise in nature by organisms that reproduce asexually.

An underground stem or root sends up new shoots as clones of the parent plant.

Members of a bacterial colony on a petri dish are clones as they came from the division of the same cell.

For many years, it was believed that adult vertebrate animals could not be cloned.

In 1996, the first cloned mammal, Dolly, a sheep, was born. Since then, other animals have been cloned.

Dolly was cloned by taking udder cells (i.e., somatic – not germline cells) from a donor sheep.

These cells were cultured in a low-nutrient medium to switch the genes off and make the cell dormant (i.e., not undergoing cellular activities as in the adult cell).

An unfertilized egg was taken from another sheep, and its nucleus was removed using a micropipette.

The egg cell was fused with the udder cells using an electric pulse.

The fused cells developed like normal zygotes and became an embryo, implanted into a "surrogate mother" sheep.

One lamb was born and named Dolly. This lamb was genetically identical to the sheep from which the udder cells were taken.

Dolly survived for almost seven years, but due to somatic cells—not germline cells—she survived for about half the average life expectancy of a sheep.

Safety and ethics of DNA technology

Genetic engineering is becoming common due to the numerous applications involved.

The advances in DNA technology have allowed for the detection of people, plants, or animals genetically prone to hereditary diseases.

Preparation for the effects of the disease or the passing of the normal gene to offspring minimizes disease.

Within the realm of bioethics, if an abnormality is detected while a fetus, it can sometimes be treated.

However, abortion is an option in these circumstances, which adds to this issue's ethical aspects.

Organisms are engineered to exhibit desirable characteristics (e.g., bacteria producing human insulin).

Infectious diseases are treated by introducing genes that encode antiviral proteins specific to an antigen.

However, there are ethical considerations.

Nature is a highly complex, interrelated chain consisting of many species linked in the food chain.

Some scientists believe that creating genetically modified organisms may have irreversible effects with unknown and potentially undesirable consequences.

Governments have produced legislation to control what experiments are performed and therapies developed that involve genetic engineering.

In some countries, strict laws prohibit any experiments involving manipulating genetic content or the cloning of humans.

People feel that it is unethical to create transgenic animals with an increased potential for suffering (e.g., a pig with no legs). Despite the ethical issues and legal restrictions, several experimental breakthroughs have been made possible by genetic engineering.

Scientists successfully manipulated the genetic sequence of a rat to grow a human ear on its back.

This was unusual but was done to reproduce human organs for medical purposes.

Therapeutic cloning of human cells (i.e., production of human embryos) could help harvest pluripotent embryonic stem cells to treat diseases. However, there are many unresolved ethical issues involved.

Arguments for and against therapeutic cloning in humans

Arguments for	*Arguments against*
Embryonic stem cells can be used for therapies that save lives and reduce pain for patients. A stem cell can divide and differentiate into cell types to replace tissues or organs required by patients.	Every human embryo is a potential human being and should be given a chance to develop.
Cells can be taken from embryos that have stopped developing, so these embryos would have died anyway.	More embryos are generally produced than are needed, so many are needlessly destroyed.
Cells are taken at a stage when the embryos have no nerve cells and cannot feel pain.	The risk of embryonic stem cells developing into tumor cells.

Genetic modifications of crops

For example, the transfer of a gene encoding the Bt toxin protein from the bacterium *Bacillus thuringiensis* to maize crops.

Maize crops are often destroyed by insects that eat the corn; adding the Bt toxin gene kills the insects. This is controversial. The table below summarizes the benefits and possible harmful effects of genetically modifying maize crops.

Benefits	*Harmful Effects*
Since there is less damage to the maize crops, there is a higher crop yield, reducing food shortages for populations.	Consumer advocates have raised concerns. The consequences of consuming modified crops are unclear. The bacterial DNA or the Bt toxin gene could be harmful to human or animal health.
Since there is a higher crop yield, less land is needed to grow more crops. Instead, the land can become an area for wildlife conservation.	Other insects not harmful to the crops could be destroyed. The maize pollen contains the toxin, and so if it is blown onto nearby plants, it kills insects feeding on the plants.
There is a reduction in pesticides, expensive and harmful to the environment, wildlife, and farmworkers.	Cross-pollination occurs, resulting in some wild plants being genetically modified with the Bt gene. These plants have an advantage as they are resistant to certain insects, causing wild plants to become endangered.

As these technologies develop, ethical issues become important to society.

Notes for active learning

Notes for active learning

REVIEW

Genetics

Mendelian Concepts of Inheritance

Mendel established the field of genetics

Gregor Mendel (1822-1884) was an Austrian monk whose experiments with plant breeding in the mid-1800s formed the basis of modern genetics. Mendel was a friar at the monastery of St. Thomas in Brunn, Austria, while teaching part-time at a local secondary school. Mendel's goal was to have firm scientific evidence for how genetic information is passed from parents to offspring. He focused on how plant offspring acquired traits from their parents. He traced the inheritance of individual traits and kept careful records of numbers, then used his understanding of probability to interpret the results.

Unfortunately, Mendel's results, published in 1865 and 1869 in the *Proceedings of the Society of Natural History of Brunn*, went mostly unnoticed until 1900. Three independent investigators, Carl Correns (Germany), Hugo De Vries (Holland), and Erich Von Tschermak (Austria), conducted similar experiments and reached the same conclusions as Mendel. After researching the literature, the three researchers gave credit to Mendel. This rediscovery and confirmation of Mendel's work launched the field of modern genetics.

Mendel chose to study the *Pisum sativum* (garden pea), as it was easy to cultivate, had a short generation time, and could be cross-pollinated by hand. Mendel chose 22 of the many pea varieties for his experiments. Concerning certain traits, the plants used in the experiment had to be *true-breeding* (progeny identical to parents). He chose this approach to ensure accuracy and simplicity in his studies.

Inbreeding genetically similar individuals obtain true-bred organisms for several generations. Pea plants can be *self-pollinated*, an effective form of inbreeding. The process eliminates genetic variation from the gene pool and results in a strain with certain identical traits in all individuals.

Mendel studied seven traits: seed shape, seed color, flower position, flower color, pod shape, pod color, and plant height. He correctly hypothesized that the inheritance pattern between generations was because the genetic information was being passed from their parents. He terms these *hereditary factors*.

Particulate theory of inheritance

The *particulate theory of inheritance* proposed by Mendel stated that factors, or "discrete particles," do not blend.

This contrasts with the *blending theory of inheritance*, discredited, which stated that offspring have traits blended from the parents. For example, red and white flowers would produce pink flowers. This is observed in nature, but the pink offspring self-fertilize and produce several all-red and all-white offspring. Proponents of the blending theory dismissed this as mere instability in genetic material.

Charles Darwin wanted to develop a theory of evolution based on hereditary principles, but the blending theory did not account for genetic variation and species diversity.

Mendel's particulate theory properly accounts for Charles Darwin's theory of evolution, although he never knew this because he did not live to see Mendel's work rediscovered. A *particulate inheritance theory* is essential for Darwin's theory of *natural selection*. Otherwise, any selectively favored trait would be blended away when the selected individual reproduced with one of a different trait.

Mendel's explanation of heredity was remarkable since it was based solely on the interpretation of breeding experiments, and it was done long before scientists understood cell division and molecular biology.

During the early part of the 20th century, the processes of mitosis and meiosis were discovered by the microscopic examination of cells. Researchers found that Mendel's hereditary factors were not free-floating particles but instead were on chromosomes in the nucleus. The hereditary factors were given the name genes.

Genes, autosomes and diploidy

A *gene* is a stretch of DNA encoding for a trait (or characteristic). Genes encode for a protein that produces a trait on a molecular level. An organism's *genome* includes its entire set of genes.

The *chromosomal theory of inheritance* states that genes are on chromosomes, and inheritance patterns are explained by the locations of genes on chromosomes.

Chromosomes are classified as autosomes and allosomes.

Autosomes are non-sex chromosomes with the same number and kind in all sexes. *Allosomes* are sex chromosomes (e.g., X or Y). Humans have 22 pairs of autosomes (44 total) and 1 pair of allosomes (2 total).

Diploidy is the characteristic of having pairs of chromosomes. One member of each pair is from the mother, and the other is from the father. *Homologous chromosomes* are similar but not identical copies.

Loci, genotype and phenotype

A *locus* is the location of a gene or segment of DNA on a chromosome. Loci are mapped by their physical position on the chromosome or by their relative distance from each other.

The loci of two homologous chromosomes are identical in their placement and align during meiosis.

Loci are identical, but the gene at a locus may be in different forms (e.g., brown eyes or blue eyes) as *alleles.* An allele is an alternative form of the gene and differs from another allele by one or more nucleotide bases that encode a specific protein.

Diploid organisms have two similar versions of each chromosome so that an individual can have a maximum of two alleles for each gene, one on each chromosome. One allele comes from the mother, and one comes from the father. Traits exhibited by an organism are determined based on the alleles an individual has inherited.

Alleles for blood types

A diploid organism inherits two alleles, but there are usually more than two alleles of each gene.

Multiple alleles are when more than two alleles encode for a characteristic. A classic example is blood type in humans. There are three blood group alleles: I^A, I^B and i.

Each can have two alleles, so the possible combinations are $I^A I^A$, $I^A i$, $I^B I^B$, $I^B i$, $I^A I^B$ and ii. An organism's combination of alleles is its *genotype.*

Genotype	Blood type (phenotype)
$I^A I^A$ or $I^A i$	A
$I^B I^B$ or $I^B i$	B
$I^A I^B$	AB
ii	O

Homozygosity and heterozygosity

Zygosity is the similarity of the alleles at any given locus.

An individual is *homozygous* for a gene when the two alleles that the individual carries are identical.

For blood types, people with the genotype $I^A I^A$, $I^B I^B$ and ii are homozygous with two identical alleles.

A *heterozygous* individual has two different alleles, as the genotypes $I^A i$, $I^B i$, and $I^A I^B$.

Wild-type and recessive phenotypes

The *wild-type allele* is the most prevalent and dominant version of the allele, with exceptions.

Mutant alleles are the product of changes in the nucleotide sequence within DNA (mutation) and are generally less common in a population.

For example, red eyes are a wild-type trait in Drosophila (fruit fly), while white eyes are the mutant trait. However, alleles often do not fit into these categories with an additional variation.

When an allele is *recessive,* the individual must inherit two copies of this allele to express the trait. The *dominant* allele is when a single copy is needed for it to be observed. A dominant allele masks (or hides) the expression of a recessive allele.

For example, the allele for attached earlobes in humans is recessive, and the allele for unattached earlobes is dominant. An individual must inherit two attached earlobe alleles to express this trait. If she inherits one attached allele and one unattached allele, the unattached allele dominates the other, leading to unattached earlobes.

By convention, the dominant allele is an uppercase letter, and the recessive allele is a lower-case letter. The letter is the first letter of the dominant or recessive allele (by convention).

For example, in Mendel's pea plants, the alleles for seed shape are named R for the dominant round allele. The recessive allele, wrinkled, is denoted *r*. However, in fruit flies, the wing size alleles are named for the recessive allele, vestigial wings.

Therefore, the dominant allele (normal wings) is denoted V and the recessive allele as v. In many cases, the locus is given one letter. The alleles are superscripts of the letter.

For example, with sex chromosomes (e.g., $X^A X^a$). Complex naming schemes are seen for multiple alleles (e.g., blood types) and co-dominant or incompletely dominant alleles (discussed later).

Genotype and phenotype

Genotype is the alleles received when an organism is conceived.

The *phenotype* describes the observable traits which are expressed. Due to recessiveness and dominance, zygosity cannot be deduced by observation of phenotype.

Two organisms with different allele combinations can have the same phenotype.

For example, if a homozygous individual has the alleles $I^A I^A$ and a heterozygous individual has the alleles $I^A i$, they have different genotypes but the same phenotype, and both exhibit blood type A since I^A is a dominant allele. Its presence overshadows the i allele in the heterozygous individual.

Mendel inferred genotype from observable phenotype by performing breeding experiments that revealed how traits emerge, disappear, and re-emerge over generations.

Traits are *characters,* and their expression in an individual is a *character state.*

Mendel streamlined his experiments by using *discontinuous* character state*s* (i.e., no intermediates).

Discontinuous traits have discrete, distinct categories; the trait is either there or not. Mendel could quantify his results by counting the two phenotypes among the offspring of each experimental cross.

Mendel's knowledge of statistics enabled him to recognize that his results followed theoretical probability calculations, even though his small sample size resulted in slight deviations from expected ratios.

Probability of inheritance

Probability is the likelihood that a given event occurs by random chance.

With a coin flip, there is a 50% chance of heads and a 50% chance of tails. In Mendelian genetics, the chance of inheriting one of two alleles from the parent is 50%.

The *multiplicative law of probability* states that the chance of two or more independent events occurring together is the product of the probability of the events occurring separately.

If two parents heterozygous for unattached earlobes (genotype Ee) have a child, the probability of the child's genotype is calculated.

In half (½) of cases, the mother passes an E allele to the child, and in the other half, she passes an e allele. The same is true for the father.

The possible combinations for the child's genotype, where one allele is inherited from the mother and another from the father:

$$EE = \tfrac{1}{2} \times \tfrac{1}{2} = \tfrac{1}{4}, \quad eE = \tfrac{1}{2} \times \tfrac{1}{2} = \tfrac{1}{4} \quad Ee = \tfrac{1}{2} \times \tfrac{1}{2} = \tfrac{1}{4} \quad ee = \tfrac{1}{2} \times \tfrac{1}{2} = \tfrac{1}{4}$$

The *additive law of probability* calculates the probability of an event that occurs in two or more independent ways; it is the sum of individual probabilities of each way an event can occur.

In the example, the chance that the child is a heterozygote is the sum of the probability of having the genotype eE (¼) or Ee (¼) = ½, or a 50% chance.

The probability of having unattached earlobes is the sum of the probabilities of inheriting at least one E (dominant) allele. This sum is ¼ + ¼ + ¼ = ¾, or a 75% chance.

Punnett square for probabilities of inheritance

These laws of probability were used in creating a method that predicts the genotypic results of genetic crosses: the *Punnett square,* introduced by R. C. Punnett.

For example, in a Punnett square, all types of alleles from the father's gametes may be aligned vertically.

All possible alleles from the mother's gametes may be aligned horizontally; possible combinations of offspring are placed in squares.

The Punnett square predicts the chance of each child's genotype and corresponding phenotype.

In genetics, probability depends on independent, mutually exclusive events.

For example, the odds of a couple having a boy or a girl is 50%.

Using the multiplicative law of probability, it is overall unlikely that a couple has 5 boys:

$$\frac{1}{2} \times \frac{1}{2} \times \frac{1}{2} \times \frac{1}{2} \times \frac{1}{2} = 1/32, \text{ or } 3.125\%.$$

However, this probability has no bearing on each event.

If the couple has four boys, there is a 50% chance their fifth child is a boy or a girl.

Each fertilization is an independent event.

In the Punnett square below, note that the mother has two copies of the X allele, while the father has one X allele and one Y allele.

In 50% of cases, the child inherits an X from the mother and an X from the father, while in the other 50% of cases, the child inherits an X from the mother and a Y from the father.

Mother

	X	X
X	XX (Girl)	XX (Girl)
Y	XY (Boy)	XY (Boy)

Father

Punnett square for the 50% probability that parents have a girl (XX) or boy (XY).

Monohybrid cross

Mendel began his experiments by creating true-breeding plants and *crossing* (mating) two true-breeding strains for alleles of the same trait.

An example is to cross a true-breeding pea plant with round seeds with another plant with wrinkled seeds; these two individuals constitute the *parental* (*P*) *generation*.

Crossbreeding is accomplished by removing the pollen-producing male organs from a "father" plant and using them to fertilize the ovary of another.

Because pea plants are *monoecious* (both male and female reproductive organs), Mendel removed the male organs from the "mother" plant to prevent self-pollinating.

The *first filial* (F1) generation is the hybrid offspring produced by this cross.

These individuals breed with one another to produce the *second filial* (F2) generation.

This is a *monohybrid cross* because it is between two individuals heterozygous for a single trait (e.g., Rr × Rr). This produces F2 offspring in a phenotypic ratio of 3:1 round to wrinkled seeds.

Example using true-breeding plants with round seeds and true-breeding plants with wrinkled seeds.

Compare results to genotype to observed phenotype ratios. **Test cross**

Proportions of a test cross with a homozygous dominant

P generation:	homozygous round (RR) × homozygous wrinkled (rr)
F1 generation:	100% heterozygous round (Rr)
F2 generation:	25% homozygous round (RR)
	50% heterozygous round (Rr)
	25% homozygous wrinkled (rr)
	Genotypic ratio: 1:2:1 RR to Rr to rr
	Phenotypic ratio: 3:1 round-seeded to wrinkle-seeded

The F2 offspring ratio is conceptualized using a Punnett square of the F1 generation cross, Rr × Rr:

	Parent 1 gametes	
	R	**r**
Parent 2 gametes — **R**	RR	Rr
r	Rr	rr

When Mendel performed this experiment with the six other traits for pea plants, he obtained similar results.

He recognized a pattern of 3:1 phenotypic ratio in the F2 generation.

Mendel extended his experimental results by inductive reasoning to claim that discontinuous traits would follow the same pattern no matter the animal or plant studied. This was how he developed the notion that each distinct phenotypic trait in an individual is controlled by two "hereditary factors" (now termed alleles).

The alternative hypothesis that each trait is controlled by one factor was not a viable explanation because it could not explain the reappearance of wrinkled seeds in the F2 generation.

These observations led him to develop the principles of dominance and recessiveness since he understood that the factor for round seeds masked the factor for wrinkled seeds.

He could have hypothesized that there are more than two hereditary factors in each. However, he used the principle of *parsimony*, which states that the simplest explanation for an observation is likely accurate.

Mendel's law of segregation

From these conclusions, Mendel was able to deduce his first law of inheritance: *the law of segregation*.

Organisms have two alleles for each trait, segregating during gamete formation for one allele per gamete.

During fertilization, gametes from two individuals are united, giving the offspring a complete set of alleles for each trait.

Although Mendel did not understand meiosis when he formulated his theories, he correctly outlined its principles in this law. He understood that if two alleles control each distinct phenotype, it follows that one is passed to the offspring by each parent. Otherwise, the number of alleles doubles with every generation.

Mendel's law of segregation is consistent with the particulate theory of inheritance because individual "discrete particles" of inheritance are passed on from generation to generation.

Dihybrid crosses

Mendel performed a *dihybrid cross* between two organisms heterozygous for two traits rather than one.

A dihybrid cross is achieved by first crossing parent organisms true-breeding for different forms of two traits; it produces F1 offspring heterozygous for both traits (dihybrids).

Mendel performed a dihybrid cross of the F1 individuals with one another.

He expected the dihybrids to produce two types of gametes: dominant (RY) and recessive (ry) gametes.

He thought he would see a phenotypic ratio of 3:1 in the F2 generation, as with his monohybrid crosses.

This means that 75% of the F2 would be round and yellow, and 25% would be wrinkled and green.

Mendel's expected Punnett square for his F1 dihybrid cross:

	RY	**ry**
RY	RRYY	RrYy
ry	RrYy	rryy

P generation:	homozygous round yellow (RRYY) × homozygous wrinkled green (rryy)
F1 generation:	100% heterozygous round yellow offspring (RrYy)
F2 generation:	25% homozygous round, homozygous yellow (RRYY)
	50% heterozygous round, heterozygous yellow (RrYy)
	25% homozygous wrinkled, homozygous green (rryy)
	Genotypic ratio: 1:2:1 RRYY to RrYy to rryy
	Phenotypic ratio: 3:1 round yellow to wrinkled green offspring

However, Mendel observed the following results from the dihybrid cross.

Parents' genotype	RRYY × rryy
Parents' gametes	RY ry
F1 generation	RrYy
F1 gametes	RY rY Ry ry

115

Punnett square of gametes produced

	RY	Ry	rY	ry
RY	RRYY	RRYy	RrYY	RrYy
Ry	RRYy	RRyy	RrYy	Rryy
rY	RrYY	RrYy	rrYY	rrYy
ry	RrYy	Rryy	rrYy	rryy

Round and yellow phenotype

Round and green phenotype

Wrinkled and yellow phenotype

Wrinkled and green phenotype

Mendel's law of independent assortment

The offspring from that cross produced a phenotypic ratio of 9:3:3:1 (of round and yellow, round and green, wrinkled and yellow, and wrinkled and green). It was not predicted that the offspring could have the dominant form of one phenotype and the recessive form of the other.

He deduced that dihybrids produce not two types of gametes (RY and ry) but *four:* RY, Ry, rY, and ry.

He realized that dominant alleles do not have to be shuffled into the same gametes as other dominant alleles, nor do recessive alleles.

Mendel's law of independent assortment states that alleles assort independently from other alleles and that a parent's gametes contain all possible combinations of alleles. This leads to a phenotypic ratio of 9:3:3:1 in dihybrid crosses. However, the ratio often breaks down in complex cases, patterns of *non-Mendelian inheritance* (do not follow Mendel's laws), for reasons that would not be understood until the 20th century.

Humans cannot be bred like pea plants, so their genetic relationships are studied using pedigrees.

Pedigree analysis

Pedigrees are charts that portray family histories by including phenotypes and family relationships. In a pedigree chart, squares represent males, circles represent females, and diamonds represent individuals of unspecified sex. If an individual displays a trait studied, their shape is filled.

Heterozygotes are half-filled (if the disorder is autosomal) or have a shaded dot inside the symbol (if the disorder is sex-linked). If the trait of interest is a disease, heterozygotes are *carriers.*

However, it is not known if an individual is heterozygous since this may not be visible phenotypically.

Lines between individuals denote relationships. Horizontal lines connect mating couples, and a vertical line connects to their offspring.

Siblings are grouped under a horizontal line that branches from this vertical one, with the oldest sibling on the left and the youngest on the right.

If the offspring are twins, they are connected by a triangle. If an individual dies, its symbol is crossed out. If it is stillborn or aborted, it is indicated by a small circle.

The generations are shown with Roman numerals (I, II, III), and each from the same generation is indicated by Arabic numbers (1, 2, 3). The pattern of inheritance of a trait is determined by analyzing pedigrees.

Often, the trait in question is a genetic disease. These are typically recessive traits seen by the way the disorder skips generations, passed by carriers.

The first family member to seek treatment for the disease is the *proband* and indicated by an arrow.

The proband serves as the starting point for the pedigree, and researchers may work backward and forward from there.

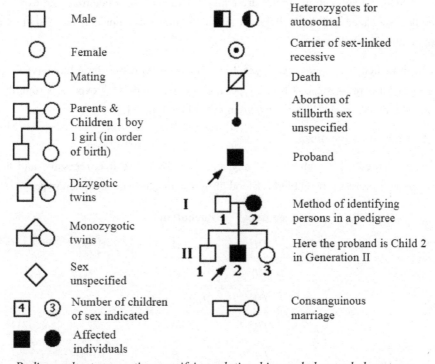

Pedigree chart convention specifying relationships and observed phenotypes

Phenotypes for complete dominance

Dominance is a relationship between alleles of one gene, in which one allele is expressed over a second allele at the same locus. Thus far, only *complete dominance* of alleles has been discussed. This occurs when only one dominant allele is needed to express a trait since it masks the recessive allele.

The traits of Mendel's pea plants had complete dominance, with a round seed shape dominating the wrinkled seed shape.

Genotype	Phenotype
RR	Dominant - round
Rr	Dominant - round
rr	Recessive - wrinkled

The homozygous dominant and heterozygous individual exhibit the "dominant phenotype," but the heterozygote has a recessive allele, though not observed.

Phenotypes for co-dominance

In *co-dominance*, two or more alleles are equally dominant, so a heterozygote expresses the phenotypes associated with both alleles. A famous example in humans is the ABO blood type system, a multiple allele system.

The locus is named "I." A person with genotype $I^A I^A$ or $I^A i$ expresses the A blood type; a person with $I^B I^B$ or $I^B i$ expresses the B blood type; and a person with $I^A I^B$ expresses roughly equal amounts of both "A" and "B" antigens, giving the blood type AB.

Thus, I^A and I^B are co-dominant.

The allele i represents the absence of any antigens. Therefore it is recessive and must be homozygous to express type O blood. Blood groups with genotype and phenotype:

Genotype	Phenotype
$I^A I^A$	*A*
$I^A I^O$	*A*
$I^A I^B$	Both *A* and *B*
$I^B I^B$	*B*
$I^B I^O$	*B*
$I^O I^O$	*O*

Phenotypes for incomplete dominance and pleiotropy

Mendel dismissed the notion that traits "blend."

Incomplete dominance (partial dominance) occurs when the phenotype of a heterozygote is an intermediate of the phenotypes of the homozygotes.

For example, true-breeding red and white-flowered four-o'clock plants produce pink-flowered offspring. The red allele is partially dominant to the white allele, so its effect is weakened and pink.

This does not support a blending theory of inheritance since the red and white parental phenotypes reappear in the F2 generation.

P   true-breeding red × true-breeding white; $(C^R C^R) \times (C^W C^W)$

F1   All pink offspring; $(C^R C^W)$

If these F1 individuals are crossed, the results are:

pink × pink; $(C^R C^W) \times (C^R C^W)$

F2   1 red: 2 pink: 1 white; $1(C^R C^R) \times 2(C^R C^W) \times (C^W C^W)$

Another example of incomplete dominance is *sickle-cell anemia*, a blood disorder controlled by incompletely dominant alleles. Homozygous dominant individuals $(Hb^A Hb^A)$ are asymptomatic and healthy.

Homozygous recessive individuals $(Hb^S Hb^S)$ are afflicted with sickle-cell anemia. Their red blood cells are irregular in shape (sickle-shaped) rather than biconcave due to abnormal hemoglobin. Sickle-shaped red blood cells clog vessels and break down, resulting in poor circulation, anemia, low resistance to infection, hemorrhaging, damage to organs, jaundice, and pain in the abdomen the joints.

This is an example of *pleiotropy*, where one gene affects many traits.

Incomplete dominance is heterozygous individuals $(Hb^A Hb^S)$ since they do not have the full-blown disease but have some sickled cells and minor health problems. This is the *sickle-cell trait*. In regions prone to malaria (e.g., Africa), being heterozygous for the sickle-cell allele confers an advantage because the malaria parasite dies as potassium leaks from sickle cells.

Heterozygote advantage describes when the heterozygote has an advantage over the homozygote.

Penetrance and expressivity

Penetrance is the frequency by which a genotype results in a corresponding phenotype.

For example, Mendel's pea plants had 100% penetrance for seed color. A plant with genotype Yy or YY had yellow seeds, and a plant with genotype yy had green seeds.

However, many genes have *incomplete penetrance.*

For example, the BRCA gene (breast cancer) for women with this mutation has an 80% lifetime risk of developing cancer. Certain people have a gene that predisposes them to lung cancer, but they may never develop cancer due to their lifestyle habits and random chance.

This means that a genotype does not guarantee that the expected phenotype is expressed in some cases.

Phenotypes can exhibit *expressivity* (variation in the presentation). This is different from penetrance (i.e., whether the phenotype is expressed). Expressivity refers to varying degrees of phenotype expression.

In *constant expressivity*, individuals with the same genotype have the same phenotype. For example, if pea plants are homozygous recessive for flower color (pp), they are approximately the same shade of white.

Discontinuous traits typically exhibit relatively constant expressivity.

However, a trait like polydactyly (i.e., extra digits) in humans is prone to *variable expressivity* when a phenotype is expressed to different degrees from the same genotype. Although a single gene controls polydactyly, afflicted individuals have extra fingers or toes. The expressivity varies from person to person.

Crossing individuals with different alleles of a continuously varying phenotype does not produce the discrete ratios that enabled Mendel to discover the laws of inheritance.

Continuous variation

The genetics of *continuous variation* is more complex than discontinuous variation (e.g., pea plants).

Such traits follow a bell-shaped curve when the number of individuals is plotted against the range of the variable trait.

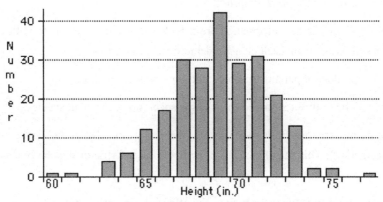

Continuous variation for height distribution in a population

With continuous variation, there is a phenotype between two chosen for comparison because the distribution of phenotypes varies along a continuum; individuals differ by small degrees.

Mendel's theory explains discontinuous and continuous patterns of individual variation.

However, with continuous variation, many different genes typically influence the same trait, not one, as Mendel proposed.

Traits such as height and weight are not due to variable expressivity of a single gene but due to *polygenic inheritance*. Polygenic inheritance is when two or more genes govern one trait.

Often, the genes have an additive effect, with each dominant allele adding to the "intensity" of the phenotype. The more genes involved, the more continuous the phenotypic variation, with a bell-shaped curve.

A human example of polygenic inheritance is skin color. Many genes control skin pigment and the more dominant alleles that an individual has, the darker their skin.

Parents with intermediate skin color can have offspring with light or dark skin.

Albinism, a condition where the eyes, skin, and hair have little to no color due to lack of pigment production, is an example of *epistasis*, a phenomenon where one gene interferes with other genes in the expression of a phenotype.

It does not matter if an individual has other genes that would otherwise give her dark skin; if the individual is homozygous recessive for the albinism gene, this shuts off pigment production and prevents the other genes from being expressed.

Traits such as height and weight have a polygenic component but are heavily influenced by outside factors, such as environment, exercise, and nutrition (nature *vs*. nurture).

Hybrids and viability

Leakage is gene flow from one species to another, which occurs when individuals of two related species mate and produce *hybrid* offspring.

The hybrid now has genetic information from both species and may mate with either one, causing genes to "leak" from each gene pool and flow into the other.

A hybrid is the product of parents true-breeding for forms of one trait.

The parents may be of different breeds of a single species or a different species.

When hybrids are created from two species, they may not always be *fertile* (capable of producing offspring). This may be because the hybrid is infertile or dies before reproductive age.

If the hybrid is fertile and able to reproduce, the offspring may prove not viable (able to survive until reproduction), known as a *hybrid breakdown.*

Hybrid vigor (heterosis) is when the hybrid has the best qualities of both species or strains.

The hybrid's superior quality is due to the suppression of recessive alleles and the increase in heterozygotic traits, leading to heterozygote advantage.

Hybrids are bred to create new breeds that are healthier or more desirable than either parent breed.

Outbreeding, population genetics and gene pool

Outbreeding is the mating of genetically dissimilar individuals and a powerful agent of genetic diversity.

Inbreeding promotes harmful recessive alleles and decreases the number of alleles in the population.

Population genetics studies the variation of alleles within a population.

The *gene pool* is the total genetic information in the population, described by gene frequencies.

Modern biologists view individuals as temporary vessels housing a small fraction of the gene pool.

Thus, the concept of a gene pool is an abstract pooling of genetic variation in the population; it does not exist apart from the individuals themselves.

Demes are local gene pools consisting of individuals likely to breed.

A great deal of evolutionary change occurs in these groups.

Meiosis and Genetic Variability of Offspring

Meiosis for genetic variability

There are several sources of genetic variability in nature, some random, while others result from selective processes. These include mutation, sexual reproduction, diploidy, outbreeding and balanced polymorphisms.

Meiosis is essential to sexual reproduction, diploidy, and genetic diversity.

Asexual organisms produce offspring as genetic clones of themselves, but sexual reproduction creates offspring similar to and unique from either parent.

Meiosis creates haploid gametes that fuse and form a diploid zygote.

Meiosis provides several opportunities to promote variability in the gene pool and allow for new combinations of alleles.

Sister chromatids and tetrads

Mitosis and meiosis begin similarly with a somatic cell in G1 of interphase, 46 chromosomes.

Chromosomes have a homologous structure that originated from the other parent; there are 23 homologous pairs, and each chromosome is scattered randomly within the nucleus. During the S phase, each chromosome duplicates.

Each duplicate is renamed a sister chromatid, and together, two sister chromatids comprise one chromosome. Sister chromatids are chromatin strands attached at the centromere, identical copies (except for low-frequency mutations of nucleotides) of the same chromosome (not homologous).

One chromosome (a pair of sister chromatids) has another chromosome, its homolog.

During prophase / metaphase of mitosis, the chromosomes do not attempt to locate their homolog. Chromosomes align along the metaphase plate individually. During anaphase, each chromosome's sister chromatids are separated so that one chromatid (resulting as a single strand separated at centromere) is partitioned into a daughter cell. The result is two diploid daughter cells with identical genetic makeup.

However, during prophase I and metaphase I of meiosis, homologs do pair into a *tetrad* (bivalent). The tetrad consists of two homologous chromosomes or four sister chromatids.

Tetrads line up on the metaphase plate so that one homologous chromosome is on one side, and the other homolog is on the other side of the midline.

During anaphase I, the tetrad is separated, and one chromosome is pulled into one pole, while the second is pulled toward the other pole. The result of meiosis I is that two daughter cells have different genetic compositions; one has half of the organism's genome and the second cell has the other half.

A key difference is that mitosis involves one set of cell divisions, in which the chromatids of each chromosome separate. In meiosis, there are two sets of cell divisions.

During the first division, the chromosome of each tetrad separates (the chromosome has 2 strands attached at the centromere). In the second division, the centromere splits, and the sister chromatids separate.

Comparing mitosis and meiosis

Mitosis	Meiosis
One set of divisions	Two sets of divisions
Occurs in body (somatic) cells	Occurs in the testes or ovaries (gametes)
Two identical daughter cells	Four unique daughter cells (four sperm cells or one egg with up to three polar bodies)
Daughter cells are diploid 2N → 2 cells with 2N	Daughter cells are haploid 2N → 4 cells with 1N
No crossing over occurs	Crossing over (tetrad) during prophase I creates genetic variability

Mendelian segregation of genes

When the homologous pairs are arranged into tetrads during meiosis, their ends overlap and cause *recombination* (i.e., exchange of genetic material).

Homologous chromosomes exchange DNA, so once separated, the maternal chromosome has some paternal DNA, and vice versa.

Gametes are unique from the organism's genome.

Mendel understood that different genes are segregated into gametes despite being unaware of meiosis.

His first *law of segregation* supports the conclusion diploid individuals have two alleles but pass one to their offspring. Segregation of genes and diploidy are important concepts for explaining genetic variability.

Independent assortment

Mendel's second law, the *law of independent assortment*, states that any gamete may have any combination of alleles. In the era of molecular biology, this occurs during meiosis.

During metaphase I of meiosis, homologous chromosomes pair as tetrads along the metaphase plate in a random orientation. They have pulled apart so that some homologous chromosomes from each parent end up in one daughter cell or another.

The law of independent assortment requires that homologous chromosomes line up randomly during metaphase. The segregation of alleles of one gene does not affect the segregation of alleles of another gene.

Mendel initially thought that a dihybrid (e.g., AaBb) produces the gametes AB and ab.

However, he realized that the A alleles and the B alleles are not linked; they can segregate into gametes in four combinations: AB, aB, Ab, and ab. He noted that these gametes are produced in equal numbers; no one combination is favored over another.

Mendel's research was based on simplistic traits of pea plants. He sometimes encountered puzzling phenotypic ratios, which suggested that some allele combinations were frequent.

If Mendel chose two phenotypic traits controlled by two tightly linked loci for his dihybrid cross, he would have obtained two types of gametes due to the *linkage*.

Gene linkage

Mendel's law of independent assortment does not apply to linkage, whereby some genes are on the same chromosome and inherited together. His law is applied to chromosomes rather than genes; chromosomes assort independently, but alleles do not.

Linked genes are close on the same chromosome, while those far apart or on different chromosomes are *unlinked genes*.

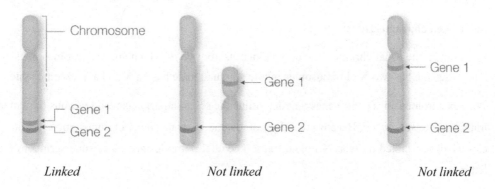

Genes on separate chromosomes are unlinked and can segregate independently, but genes on the same chromosome are often inherited together as a *linkage group*. However, this is not always true.

Crossing over and recombination

Crossing over allows genes on the same chromosome to become unlinked due to the probability that the genes undergo recombination in the region between them.

Genetic recombination introduces genetic diversity into the gametes during meiosis. It includes independent assortment and crossing over. Crossing over occurs during prophase I of meiosis when homologous chromosomes are paired into tetrads.

The pairing of tetrads is *synapsis* and is facilitated by a protein structure of the *synaptonemal complex*. It is thought that the synaptonemal complex functions primarily as a scaffold to allow interacting chromatids to complete their crossover activities.

During prophase I, synapsis links the four sister chromatids (4 strands with 2 chromosomes) of a homologous chromosome pair. The ends of separate chromatids often overlap and make contact at sites, as *chiasmata*, between loci.

Both chromatids cut at the same locus, allowing them to bind where they are cut (chiasma) and swap their DNA. In this way, an individual can create gametes with some chromatids different from the chromatids they inherited.

Recombinants are chromatids that have undergone recombination, and those which did not are *parental*.

Once crossing over is finished, the homologous chromosomes are no longer tightly linked, and the homologous chromosomes are independent. However, the recombinant chromatids remain connected by their chiasma until anaphase, when the centromeres divide and liberate each sister chromatid strand, which becomes a chromosome.

Sex-linked characteristics

In a human, the usual chromosome complement is 46, two of which are sex chromosomes. A human female has two X chromosomes, while a human male has an X and a Y chromosome.

The sex chromosomes carry genes that determine the sex of an organism and various unrelated traits that are *sex-linked*. Because the Y chromosome is small, the X chromosome essentially carries all sex-linked traits as X-linked traits. The alleles are designated as superscripts to the letter X.

In females, one of the duplicate X chromosomes is deactivated during embryonic development, resulting in an unused chromosome, a *Barr body*. This is random in cells, so in one cell, the paternal X chromosome may become the Barr body, while in another, the maternal X chromosome becomes the Barr body.

In males, chromosomes X and Y do not make a homologous pair since they are of various sizes and contain different genes. The X chromosome in humans is longer than the Y chromosome and contains many genes. The smaller Y chromosome has no opposing alleles to those on the X chromosome in a male.

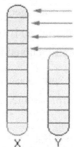

Males are *hemizygous* for X-linked traits, meaning they have one allele since they have one X chromosome. In the pairing seen below, genes on the X chromosome with an arrow pointing to them are dominant because they have no opposition from the Y chromosome. There are genes with loci on the X and Y chromosomes.

Males are prone to certain genetic diseases due to this characteristic. A female inheriting a sex-linked recessive allele encoding for a genetic disease may inherit the other X chromosome's dominant allele. She is unafflicted (i.e., complete dominance) or has minor afflictions (incomplete or co-dominance). However, a male has no such mitigating protection and is affected by the single x-linked trait.

Y chromosome genes and sex determination

The Y chromosome is significantly smaller than the X chromosome and contains a lower density of genes, perhaps 50 to 60. However, these few genes have an important impact on sex determination and male characteristics.

Genes on the Y chromosomes that do not recombine are passed from father to son and are not present in females. The lack of recombination weakens natural selection effectiveness to reduce the frequency of disadvantaged variants and select for favorable ones.

Humans have an *XY sex-determination system*. Most other mammals, along with some insects and fish, follow this. Females produce gametes with a single X chromosome, while sperm from the male can contain a Y chromosome or an X chromosome.

There is a 50% chance that a gamete contains either chromosome. Therefore, when the gametes fuse during fertilization, there is a 50% chance of a female (or male) sex.

The maternal gamete is *homogametic* because its cells possess the XX sex chromosomes. Sperm gametes are the variable factor and are thus *heterogametic* because around half contain the X chromosome, and the other half possess the Y chromosome.

In the absence of a Y chromosome, genes on the X chromosomes direct a fetus to produce female sex hormones and develop internal and external female sex organs. However, if a Y chromosome is present, its *SRY gene* inhibits female sex organs' development and promotes male sex organs.

The SRY gene is powerful since it controls other genes' activity, directing the development of internal and external male characteristics. Gene mutations can cause the fetus to develop nonfunctional testes or ovaries.

In some cases, errors during the male production of gametes attach the SRY gene to an X chromosome. This results in a female fetus developing male phenotypic characteristics.

Note that many other organisms have different sex determination schemes. For example, in an *XO sex determination system* females have two X chromosomes, and males have one. In a *ZW sex-determination system* (e.g., birds, reptiles, and many other organisms), the males have two Z chromosomes, while females have a Z and a W chromosome. Several other sex-determination systems involve different chromosomes, often more than two; for example, platypuses each have ten sex chromosomes.

In many reptiles and invertebrates, sex is determined not by genetics but by environmental factors (e.g., temperature). Some species can change sex throughout their lifetime.

Cytoplasmic and extranuclear inheritance

Extranuclear inheritance, known as *cytoplasmic inheritance,* is the inheritance of genetic material found outside the nucleus. This was discovered by Carl Correns in 1908. The two most prevalent examples are the inheritance of mitochondria and chloroplasts in many eukaryotes. Along with the nuclear chromosomes, DNA from the mitochondria (and chloroplasts for plants) are transferred in the cytoplasm of the maternal gamete. Sperm contains these organelles as well, but they either do not enter the egg during fertilization or do enter but are destroyed by the egg. Therefore, extranuclear DNA is always passed along the maternal line, making it useful for certain genetic testing.

DNA nucleotide sequence mutations

Mutations are changes in the DNA nucleotide sequence that arise by means other than recombination. Mutant genes may produce abnormalities in structure and function, leading to disease.

Cystic fibrosis, sickle-cell anemia, hemophilia, and muscular dystrophy are *single-gene diseases* because they arise from mutations in a single gene.

Polygenic diseases, such as diabetes, cancer, cleft lip, and schizophrenia, result from several defective genes that have little effect on their own but collectively can have significant effects. The environment greatly influences many genetic disorders, physical features, and behavioral traits.

Genetic mutations can be beneficial, neutral, or harmful.

Beneficial or *advantageous mutations* provide an improvement to the fitness of the organism.

Deleterious mutations disrupt gene function and result in a harmful effect on the fitness of the organism. Mutations can be harmful in one situation but advantageous in another.

Neutral mutations have a negligible effect on fitness, neither harmful nor beneficial. Mutations may not affect the phenotype as *silent mutations,* or the effect does not arise until later generations.

Random mutations are changes in the DNA sequence due to radiation, chemicals, replication errors, or other chance events.

Transcription errors occur specifically during the transcription of DNA into mRNA. This results in mRNA with some RNA nucleotide sequences that do not accurately correspond to the original DNA code.

Translation errors occur during the translation of mRNA into a protein by a mutant amino acid sequence.

Classifying mutations

Base substitutions are when another replaces one or more nucleotides. They range from advantageous to fatal (as with many mutations), but most base substitutions are minor.

Nucleotide base substitutions may cause a stop codon to halt transcription, a *nonsense mutation.*

Substitutions could cause a different amino acid to be transcribed in the protein, causing a *missense mutation.* A single amino acid change may change the protein's function or render it inoperable.

However, since some mRNA codons can encode for the same amino acid (i.e., code is degenerative), sometimes base substitutions may not result in a different amino acid sequence.

Silent mutations do not affect the phenotype.

Deletions involve a base (or several bases) being removed from the DNA or mRNA sequence, while *insertions* involve adding one (or more) bases.

One or two insertions (or deletions) result in *frameshift mutations* by shifting the reading frame of the three-base codons.

For example, the mRNA sequence AUGUUGACUGCCAAU is meant to be read:

AUG - UU<u>G</u> - ACU - GCC – A …

Met - Leu - Thr - Ala - …

If the 6th base (guanine) is deleted, a frameshift mutation changes the transcribed amino acids.

AUG - UUA - CUG - CCA - …

Met - Leu - Leu - Pro - …

The first codon is unaffected and still encodes for methionine. The second codon *is* changed, but since this codon encodes for the same amino acid (leucine), it is a silent mutation.

However, the third and fourth codons are changed to encode different amino acids. It is assumed that many other amino acids in the sequence are changed. This is a severe mutation rendering the protein inoperable.

However, deletions and insertions of nucleotides that involve multiples of threes do not cause a frameshift since they remove an entire codon (i.e., three nucleotides that encode an amino acid). The reading frame remains intact, but the absence of a single amino acid may be a serious issue.

Repetitive sequences and gene duplication

Slipped-strand mispairing is a mutation that occurs during transcription, translation, or DNA replication. After DNA strands are denatured during replication, the template or replicated strand may slip (become temporarily dislodged) and cause incorrect pairing of complementary bases. This is believed to have led to the evolution of many repetitive DNA sequences in the human genome.

Portions of the chromosome are subject to deletion, especially during meiosis. Chromosomal deletion may be severe and renders the gamete incapable of fertilization or spontaneous abortion.

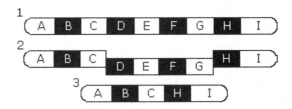

Chromosomal deletion where sections D, E, F, and G are absent after deletion

Chromosomal inversions and translocation

Along with base mutations, the chromosome's entire structure is subject to rearrangement, especially during meiosis. Chromosomal mutations may be severe or fatal, terminating the fetus before birth.

Inversions involve a stretch of DNA breaking and reattaching in the opposite orientation.

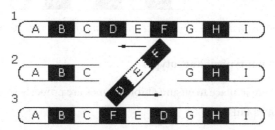

Two types of inversions are paracentric and pericentric.

Paracentric inversions do not involve the centromere; they occur when a piece of the arm of chromosome breaks, inverts and reattaches.

A *pericentric inversion* includes the centromere; the breakpoint is on either arm of the chromosome.

The organism experiencing the newly inverted sequence may not be viable if it includes a necessary chromosome region. The mutation could be advantageous. However, inversions usually do not affect the organism's phenotype and go undetected. Their greatest impact is on the production of gametes since they are often marked by loops in the chromosome that affects recombination.

An individual with a chromosomal inversion may generate gametes with altered linkage relationships or abnormal chromatids. The former case is likely harmless, while the latter usually yields inviable gametes.

Translocation is when a segment of one chromosome separates and binds to the other. This is a drastic rearrangement that is often lethal. An individual inheriting a chromosome that has been altered due to translocation has extra alleles or too few alleles, leading to a variety of defects. This may occur in autosomal and sex chromosomes, leading to infertility issues and other genetic disorders.

XX male syndrome occurs when the portion of the Y chromosome containing the SRY gene is translocated to an X chromosome during a male's gamete production. If the sperm cell containing the mutant X chromosome fertilizes an egg, a female fetus develops male secondary sex characteristics and genitalia.

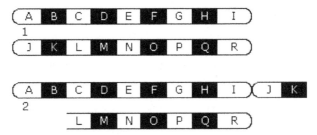

Chromosomal translocation where section J and K join the other chromosome

Nondisjunction and nontypical karyotypes

Although safeguards are in place to ensure chromosomes are properly separated during meiosis, these checks sometimes fail.

Failure of proper chromosome separation causes *nondisjunction errors,* in which three chromosomes of a tetrad are pulled to one side of the spindle, and one is pulled to the other side. This results in gametes having an extra chromosome and gametes lacking a chromosome.

A chromosome with three copies is *trisomy*, while a chromosome with one copy is *monosomy*. Both examples of gamete formation by nondisjunction usually lead to an inviable zygote.

Down syndrome is a common nonlethal autosomal trisomy involving chromosome 21. In general, the chance of a woman having a Down syndrome child increases with age. This disorder leads to faster aging, moderate to severe developmental issues, and a higher risk of health complications.

Many nonlethal nondisjunction errors involve the sex chromosomes.

Females with *Turner syndrome* have one X sex chromosome. This results in nonfunctional ovaries and the absence of puberty. Afflicted females have somewhat masculine characteristics and sterile but usually have no cognitive issues using hormone therapy.

Klinefelter syndrome occurs when a zygote receives one Y chromosome and two (or more) X chromosomes. The Y chromosome makes affected individuals identifiably male, but they have underdeveloped sex organs and are sterile.

The extra X chromosomes cause the development of breasts, lack of facial hair, and cognitive delay.

Males with Klinefelter syndrome have one or more Barr bodies due to the extra X chromosomes.

Karyotypes

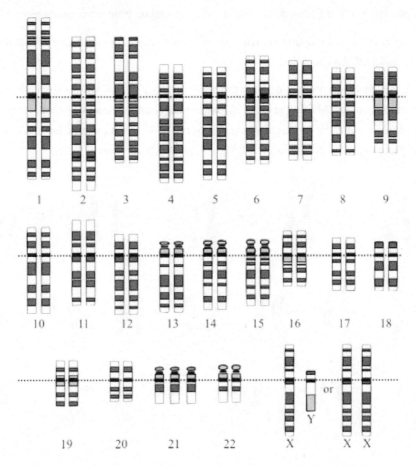

Karyotype of a male patient with Down syndrome (three chromosomes, 21) and an extra set of X chromosomes (XXXY) as a variant of Klinefelter syndrome (XXY)

Females with *Poly-X syndrome* have extra X chromosomes and extra Barr bodies. They do not exhibit enhanced feminine characteristics and appear physically normal. Some experience menstrual irregularities, but most have regular menstruation and are fertile. Females with three X chromosomes are not developmentally delayed but have impaired cognitive skills. However, four X chromosomes cause severe cognitive impairment.

Jacob's syndrome is one X chromosome and two Y chromosomes. Although it was previously believed that individuals with Jacob's syndrome were likely to be aggressive, this claim is refuted.

Males with Jacob's syndrome are taller than average, suffer from persistent acne, and tend to have speech and reading problems.

Many genetic disorders, especially from nondisjunction, can be detected during pregnancy. Chorionic villi sampling testing, amniocentesis, and karyotyping are prenatal testing methods.

Karyotyping (visual examination of chromosomes) determines the gender of a fetus and surveys for chromosomal abnormalities.

The sex chromosome structure deduces the gender since Y chromosomes are markedly smaller than X chromosomes. Missing or extra chromosomes visualize nondisjunction. If there are two of each chromosome, the 23 chromosome pairs result in 46 chromosomes. Deviations from this, such as three copies of chromosome 21, signifies a nondisjunction.

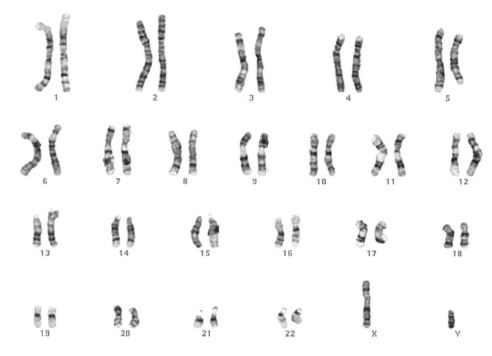

Karyotype of a typical male patient

Inborn errors of metabolism

Inborn errors of metabolism are genetic disorders that cause mild to severe metabolic issues. These diseases are caused by a mutant gene that results in abnormal enzyme production, affecting the gastrointestinal system, the circulatory system, the nervous system, or any area of the body.

They are typically rare and have severe health implications.

However, benign inborn errors of metabolism, such as lactose intolerance, arise from an inability to produce the digestive enzyme lactase.

Unlike many genetic disorders, inborn errors of metabolism are caused by a single gene mutation.

Autosomal recessive disorders

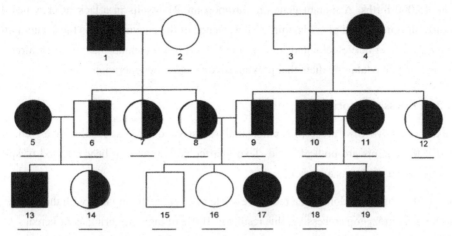

Pedigree for autosomal recessive: squares denote males, circles denote females; shaded figures are afflicted, while half-filled figures are carriers

Autosomal recessive disorders are discerned from pedigrees by establishing the presence of specific patterns of inheritance. The first observation is that affected children usually have unaffected carrier parents since recessive alleles are statistically rare in the general population.

Two homozygous dominant parents produce unaffected children.

However, if one parent is affected, the children are unaffected carriers. If one parent is affected and the other is a carrier, they have a 50% chance of producing a carrier child or affected child as in the pedigree chart. Note the many carriers (half-filled circles or squares) due to their affected parents.

Individuals 15 and 16 (third generation) may be homozygous dominant or carriers. Genetic testing reveals if they inherited two dominant alleles from each carrier parent or a dominant allele from one and a recessive allele from the other parent.

Tay-Sachs disease is an autosomal recessive disorder rare in the general population but afflicts approximately 1 in 3,600 Ashkenazi Jews at birth. Tay-Sachs results in death by about age three due to progressive neurological degeneration. A genetic mutation prevents the production of the enzyme hexosaminidase A (Hex A), leading to accumulations of its substrate, glycosphingolipid, in lysosomes of brain cells. Tay-Sachs is one of many *lysosomal storage disorders* caused by abnormal lysosomal function.

Cystic fibrosis is a common lethal genetic disease in Northern European ancestry. About 1 in 20 Caucasians in the U.S. is a carrier for cystic fibrosis, and about 1 in 3,000 is afflicted. The disease is caused by a mutation of chromosome 7 that prevents chloride ions from passing into some cells. Since water normally follows Cl^-, a lack of water in lung cells causes viscous mucus and subsequent respiratory issues. This disease has gastrointestinal, kidney, and fertility effects.

135

Phenylketonuria (PKU) is a common inherited disease of the nervous system, occurring once in about 15,000 births. A mutant gene on chromosome 21 results in a lack of enzymes that metabolize the amino acid phenylalanine. The absence of the enzyme causes the accumulation of phenylalanine in nerve cells and impairs the CNS. From neonatal diagnosis, children are placed on low-phenylalanine diets that prevent severe neural degeneration.

Sex-linked recessive disorders

Sex-linked recessive disorders, like autosomal recessive disorders, results in all children affected if the parents are both affected. Two unaffected parents can bear affected offspring (male only) if the mother is a carrier.

She has a 50% chance of donating a recessive allele to a son, afflicting him with the disease. If the mother is homozygous recessive, this results in 100% of male offspring as affected.

Female offspring are unaffected as the father donates a dominant X-linked allele; but, all are carriers.

If an affected male mates with a homozygous dominant female, offspring are unaffected. However, if the father is affected and the mother is a carrier, 50% of their children, regardless of sex, are affected.

Color blindness is an X-linked recessive disorder involving mutations of genes coding for green-sensitive pigment or red-sensitive pigment; the gene for blue-sensitive pigment is autosomal. About 8% of Caucasian men have red-green color blindness.

Duchenne muscular dystrophy is the common form of muscular dystrophy and is characterized by the wasting (atrophy) of muscles, eventually leading to death. It affects 1 in 3,600 male births. This X-linked recessive disease involves a mutant gene that fails to produce the protein dystrophin. The lack of dystrophin promotes an enzyme that dissolves muscle fibers. Affected males rarely live to be fathers; the allele survives in the population due to transmission by carrier females.

About 1 in 10,000 males is a hemophiliac with an impaired blood clotting ability. This is a classic example of an X-linked recessive disorder, famously seen in the royal families of Europe throughout the 19th and 20th centuries.

Queen Victoria was a carrier of the disease and passed it on to many of her descendants. Due to diplomatic marriages within a small subpopulation, it was transmitted to royal families in Russia, Germany, and Spain. The issue was exacerbated by incest, not uncommon, to keep power and assets within the family.

Autosomal dominant disorders

Autosomal dominant disorders are discerned from pedigrees by establishing the presence of certain patterns. The first is that affected children must have an affected parent. Two affected parents can have an unaffected child if both parents are heterozygous.

However, two unaffected parents cannot have a child that is affected.

As with autosomal disorders, males and females are affected with equal frequency.

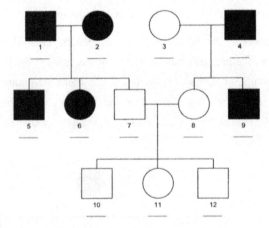

Pedigree for autosomal dominant: circles denote females, squares denote males;
filled shapes are affected individuals, while unfilled shapes are not carriers of the disorder

Neurofibromatosis is an autosomal dominant disorder in about 1 in 3,500 people. It is caused by an altered gene on chromosome 17 that controls the production of the neurofibromin protein, which normally inhibits cell division. When this gene is mutated, neurofibromin is nonfunctional, and affected individuals develop neurofibromas, benign skin tumors. In most cases, symptoms are mild, and patients live healthy lives but can be severe.

Since the severity of symptoms varies, this is an example of *variable expressivity*.

Huntington's disease is an autosomal dominant disorder that, while fatal, usually does not onset until middle age, after an afflicted individual may already have children. Therefore, the disease continues to pass through the generations. The gene for Huntington's disease is on chromosome 4.

This gene encodes the *huntingtin protein* as extra glutamine in the amino acid sequence, causing the mutant huntingtin protein to form clumps inside neurons.

Achondroplasia is a form of dwarfism caused by defective bone growth in about 1 in 25,000 people. People with achondroplasia have short limbs, a deformed spine, and an average torso and head. Like many genetic disorders, being homozygous dominant for achondroplasia is lethal; afflicted individuals are heterozygotes.

Sex-linked dominant disorders

Sex-linked dominant disorders have characteristics distinguished from other inherited genetic disorders, which is discerned by analyzing a pedigree.

If a male is affected, his female offspring are affected because he donates an affected X chromosome to his female offspring. Since the allele is dominant, offspring are affected.

By contrast, male offspring are affected if the mother has the disease because the father donates a Y chromosome (does not carry the gene) to his male offspring.

Unlike autosomal genetic disorders, sex-linked genetic disorders affect the sexes disproportionately, as in the pedigree below. There are no carriers since having one dominant allele signifies affliction. Like autosomal dominant disorders, dominant sex-linked disorders are not common in the population since they lead to health problems that reduce the reproduction frequency. This makes the alleles rarer in the gene pool, a self-fulfilling cycle that keeps them at a low frequency.

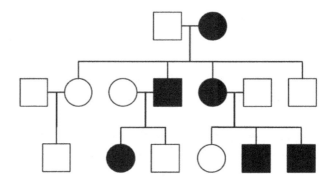

Pedigree for dominant sex-linked disorder: squares denote males, circles denote females; filled shapes are afflicted individuals, while unfilled are healthy individuals

The *fragile X syndrome* is an X-linked dominant disorder in which the *FMR1* gene is mutated. This causes a deficiency of the protein FMRP protein, affecting neural and physical development. The mutation is found among both sexes, though it is prevalent in females. Affected children often have hyperactive behaviors, intellectual disabilities, and autism spectrum disorders. Although about one-fifth are unaffected due to incomplete penetrance, these symptoms are severe in males.

Pedigrees and test crosses

Pedigrees must determine sex-linked traits in humans since it is not ethical to orchestrate human mating, while other organisms are bred to determine patterns of inheritance.

In non-humans, a *reciprocal cross* involves two sets of parents, in which the male and female have opposite traits. For example, in one set, a female pea plant has white flowers, and the male has purple flowers, and in another, the female has purple flowers, and the male has white flowers. This determines the inheritance of sex-linked traits.

If the trait is autosomal, both crosses produce the same results; if not, they produce different results.

Test cross uses the homozygous recessive to mate with an organism of known phenotype but unknown genotype. If progeny resemble the known phenotype parent, the parent is homozygous dominant.

A 50:50 ratio means that the parent is heterozygous for the phenotypic trait.

For example, AA × aa = Aa and Aa × aa = Aa and aa.

Mutagens and carcinogens

The genetic component of cancers is the leading cause of death in developed nations and the second leading cause in developing nations. Most cancers are caused by a genetic predisposition and by carcinogens.

Carcinogens are any physical, chemical, or biological agents that cause cancer.

The majority of carcinogens are *mutagens,* harmful agents that cause DNA mutations.

Toxic chemicals, radiation, free radicals, viruses, and bacteria are possible mutagens.

Exogenous mutagens come from an external event, like smoking a cigarette or exposing one's skin to UV radiation.

Endogenous mutagens arise internally as byproducts of metabolic processes. *Reactive oxygen species* (ROS) are a class of endogenous mutagens containing oxygen and are highly reactive (e.g., H_2O_2 and O^{-2}).

Mitogens are another class of carcinogens that trigger an increase in mitosis rate. While carcinogens are mutagens or mitogens, there are mutagens and mitogens that do not lead to cancer.

Genetic drift, founder effect and inbreeding

Genetic drift refers to random changes in allele frequencies of a gene pool over time. This occurs in large and small populations, but the effect is magnified in small populations. Isolated gene pools can quickly diverge from the parent population. Over time, large populations may speciate (organisms cannot reproduce to produce viable and fertile offspring).

Genetic drift causes alleles to be lost and others to become *fixed,* meaning they are the only allele for a gene in the population. Variation among populations can often be attributed to the random effects of genetic drift.

The *founder effect* is an example of genetic drift, whereby a handful of founders leave a source population and establish a colony. The new population contains a fraction of the total genetic diversity of the original population. Over time, the founders' alleles may occur at high frequencies in the new population, even if they are rare in the original population. For example, cases of dwarfism are high in the Pennsylvania Amish community because a few German founders were dwarfs.

The *bottleneck effect* may occur after excessive predation, habitat destruction, or a natural disaster rather than a founding event. After the catastrophe, there is a major decrease in the total genetic diversity of the original gene pool.

Purely by chance, alleles are lost, and this affects the future genetic makeup of the population. Today, relative infertility is found in cheetahs due to a bottleneck in earlier times. Small populations suffer low genetic variation due to the high rates of inbreeding.

Genetic drift is a random process, greatly enhanced when other genetic diversity agents are random. Random mating, in which individuals pair by chance and not by any selection, is one example. However, most populations practice nonrandom mating, which inhibits genetic diversity.

Inbreeding, where relatives mate, can occur as nonrandom mating because they are near others.

Assortative mating occurs when individuals mate with those that have similar phenotypes. This may divide a population into two phenotypic classes with reduced gene exchange.

Phenotypes can be selected due to *sexual selection* when males compete for the right to reproduce, and (often) the females select males based on phenotype.

Gene flow and genetic variation

Gene flow is the introduction (or removal) of alleles from populations when individuals leave (emigration) or enter the population (immigration).

Gene flow increases variation within a population by introducing novel alleles from another population.

Continued gene flow decreases variation between populations, causing their gene pools to become similar. Because of this, gene flow is a powerful opposing force in speciation.

Balanced polymorphisms and frequency-dependent selection

Balanced polymorphisms add to genetic variability by maintaining two different alleles in the population rather than encouraging homozygosity. Balanced polymorphisms are maintained by heterozygote advantage, hybrid vigor, and frequency-dependent selection.

Frequency-dependent selection is when the frequency of one phenotype affects the frequency of another.

For example, a prey animal population may have several coloring phenotypes in the population (e.g., gray, brown, black fur). When the gray phenotype becomes frequent in the population, predators become familiar with this phenotype and can identify prey by their gray fur.

Natural selection makes it so that the rarer phenotypes (brown and black fur) have an advantage.

Prey evolve these phenotypes until one becomes common, with frequency-dependent selection changes.

This is *minority advantage* when the rarest phenotype has the highest fitness (i.e., chance of survival).

Phenotypes can have a positive frequency-dependent relationship from safety in numbers.

For example, individuals of a poisonous species may evolve coloring that signals their toxicity. Predators learn this signal and avoid individuals with this phenotype.

In this example, it is a disadvantage to have a unique phenotype that is not identifiable as poisonous because these individuals have an increased probability of being eaten by predators.

Synapsis (crossing-over) for increasing genetic diversity

It is hypothesized that meiosis evolved from either the bacterial analog of sexual reproduction (transformation) or from mitosis. It is ubiquitous in eukaryotes and is the source of genetic variation in sexual reproduction. Recombination creates recombinant chromosomes, and then meiosis independently sorts chromosomes into different gametes.

Suppose a woman inherited the alleles A and b from her mother and a and B from her father. She has genotype AaBb. Her alleles are not necessarily arranged in a *cis* configuration:

$$\frac{A\ B}{a\ b}$$

The top alleles (AB) represent one chromosome, and the bottom (ab) represent its homolog inherited from the other parent.

She could have inherited the alleles on the chromosomes as a *trans* configuration:

$$\frac{A\ b}{a\ B}$$

It is not possible to know from her phenotype alone what configuration (*cis* or *trans*) she has, since both results in the same phenotype. One must know her parents' genotypes or perform statistical analysis of her children's phenotypes. However, a sample size in the hundreds would be required to make the latter strategy accurate, which is improbable. Her configuration is determined by her parents' gametes and influences how she produces gametes.

Suppose she is *cis* (AB / ab), and the genes are closely linked. When she produces gametes, the crossover is unlikely because the genes are close together. Each somatic cell divides into the four gametes: AB, AB, ab, and ab. She has produced all parental chromosomes since they are identical to herself (parental). However, if the alleles are farther apart, there is the increased probability of crossover.

Crossover allows a *cis* configuration to become a *trans* configuration or vice versa. A *single crossover* is a crossing-over between two adjacent non-sister chromatids of a tetrad, at only a single chiasma. The two chromatids which crossed over are recombinant, while the other two remain parental (nonrecombinant). The following image illustrates a tetrad that has undergone recombination to produce some recombinant chromatids.

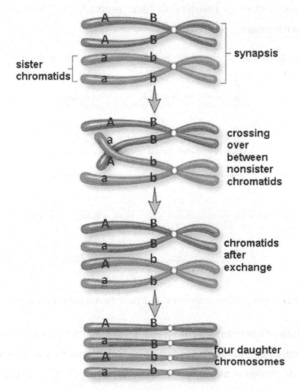

Crossing over with exchange at tetrad with A for a.
From AB and ab, the four gametes produced are AB, aB, Ab and ab

A *double crossover* is more complicated and can have a few different outcomes. A *two-stranded* double crossover involves two chromatids that overlap each other at two points. They exchange alleles at first, but then exchange them back, resulting in no net recombination. When a crossover occurs between alleles, the following summaries are accurate. Although each chromatid ends up with a region of the other, these are noncoding regions between the loci, so the crossing-over has no observable difference. This results in four parental chromatids.

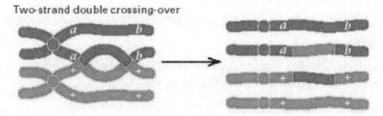

Double crossover results from two exchanges and preserves the parental genotype
chromosomes

A *three-stranded* double crossover involves three chromatids of two chromosomes. Like a single crossover, this results in two recombinants and two parentals.

143

A *four-stranded* double crossover involves all four chromatids in the tetrad. It results in four recombinants and no parentals.

If the crossover event flanks an allele on each side, the following is observed:

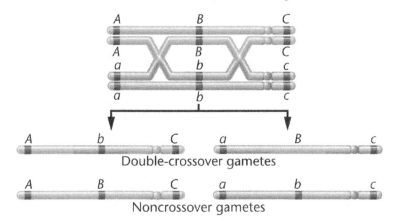

Double-crossover gametes

Noncrossover gametes

The result is two noncrossover chromosomes and two recombinant chromosomes.

The random orientation of homologous chromosomes during metaphase I and their independent assortment into separate daughter cells is another important mechanism of recombination. The number of possible orientations at the metaphase plate is equal to 2^n, where n is the haploid number of chromosomes.

Since humans have a haploid number of 23, they have 2^{23} possible outcomes, yielding over 8,388,000 possible combinations of gametes from the division of a single cell. Compounded with the effects of exchange of genetic material on a chromosome during crossing over, the number of combinations increases even further to virtually infinite genetic variety.

Summary of important terms in genetics

Carrier - an individual that has one copy of a recessive allele that causes a genetic disease in individuals that are homozygous for this allele.

Codominant alleles - pairs of alleles that both affect the phenotype when present in a heterozygote.

Dominant allele - an allele that has the same effect on the phenotype, whether it is present in the homozygous or heterozygous state.

Genotype - the alleles of an organism.

Heterozygous - having two different alleles of a gene.

Homozygous - having two identical alleles of a gene.

Locus - the particular position of a gene on a chromosome.

Phenotype - the characteristics of an organism.

Analytic Methods

Hardy-Weinberg principle

In the 1930s, scientists were able to apply genetics to populations and observe the small-scale evolution of a gene pool.

A population in stasis has constant gene frequencies and is in *Hardy-Weinberg equilibrium*. This provides a baseline by which to judge whether evolution has occurred. Populations can only be in Hardy-Weinberg equilibrium if they meet the requirements of the *Hardy-Weinberg principle*. These assumptions describe a population without changes in allelic and genotypic frequencies, due to the absence of evolutionary pressures. The conditions are as follows:

1) Mutation does not occur at any significant rate.

2) Gene flow is absent as individuals do not migrate among populations.

3) Nonrandom mating does not occur; individuals pair by chance and do not engage in mate selection.

4) Genetic drift is minimal; the population is large, so changes in allele frequencies due to chance are insignificant.

5) Natural selection does not occur; the population does not experience competition, and no traits have a selective advantage.

In the natural world, the conditions of the Hardy-Weinberg principle are rarely, if ever, met, so allelic and genotypic frequencies change, and thus evolution occurs.

The Hardy-Weinberg principle includes mathematical models to predict frequencies.

1) Allele frequencies: $p + q = 1$, represented by p and q, sum to 100% in the gene pool.

2) Genotype frequencies: $p^2 + 2pq + q^2 = 1$, which arise from the two alleles, sum to 100% in the gene pool. The homozygous dominant genotype (pp) equals the product of $p \times p$ (or p^2). The homozygous recessive genotype (qq) equals the product of $q \times q$ (or q^2). The heterozygous genotype is represented by two possibilities, pq, and qp, and therefore is the sum of both their products (or $2pq$).

Example: A plant population has two phenotypes for flower color: the wild-type red and the white mutant phenotype. The wild-type red flowers are inherited from at least one dominant allele (R), and the mutant white flowers are inherited from two recessive alleles (r). In this gene pool, 84% of the flowers have the red phenotype, and 16% have the white phenotype. What are the frequencies of the alleles? What are the frequencies of the genotypes?

Solution:

Assume that the red allele (R) is "*p*" and the white allele (r) is "*q*."

Since the frequency of the white phenotype is 16%, then $q^2 = 0.16$. This is the frequency of the homozygous recessive genotype.

Since the frequency of the red phenotype is 84%, then $p^2 + 2pq = 0.84$. Remember that p^2 and $2pq$ are the homozygous dominant and heterozygous genotypes, respectively. Together, they represent the wild-type (red) phenotype.

Solving for the white allele, *q*:

$$q = \sqrt{q^2} = \sqrt{0.16} = 0.4$$

Therefore, the frequency of the white allele in the population is 0.4 (or 40%).

Solving for the red allele, *p*:

$$p + q = 1$$

$$p = 1 - q$$

$$p = 1 - 0.4 = 0.6$$

Therefore, the frequency of the red allele in the population is 0.6 (or 60%).

Solving for p^2:

$$p^2 = 0.6^2 = 0.36.$$

The frequency of the homozygous dominant genotype is 36%.

Solving for $2pq$:

$$2pq = 0.84 - p^2$$

$$2pq = 0.84 - 0.36$$

$$2pq = 0.48.$$

The frequency of the heterozygous genotype is 48%.

Experimental Methods in Genetics

Testcross determines parental genotype

A *test cross* is the mating of an individual with an unknown genotype against an individual with a homozygous recessive genotype. This may be done for one or more traits. Mendel used this to ensure his plants were true-breeding.

For example, Mendel may have had a plant with white flowers (a recessive trait), so he knew it was homozygous recessive for white flowers; genotype pp.

Another plant may have had purple flowers, but he could not be sure whether it was Pp or PP since this is the dominant phenotype.

He crossed the purple (known phenotype but unknown genotype) plant with the white plant.

The phenotypic results of a test cross indicate the presence of the genotypes even though the genotypes (PP or Pp) could not be observed phenotype is observed.

Example: A white-flowered pea plant (genotype pp) and an unknown, purple-flowered pea plant (genotype P) are test-crossed to determine the genotype (PP or Pp) of the purple parent.

To analyze a test cross of a white plant and an unknown purple plant, establish the possible gametes.

Probability used for testcross analysis

Since the white parent is a homozygote (pp), there is a 100% probability that it contributes a p allele and a 0% probability that it contributes a P allele; every gamete contains a p allele.

If the purple parent is a homozygote (PP), there is a 100% probability of contributing a P allele to its offspring and a 0% probability of contributing a p allele.

The likelihood that their offspring are genotype Pp is $1.0 \times 1.0 = 1.0$ (or 100%) from probability.

The probability of genotype PP is 0%, and the probability of genotype pp is 0%; offspring are Pp to exhibit the phenotype of a purple flower.

However, if the purple parent is a heterozygote (Pp), there is a 50% probability of contributing a p allele and a 50% probability of contributing a P allele.

Therefore, the probability of having offspring with genotype Pp is $1.0 \times 0.5 = 50\%$.

The probability of genotype pp is $1.0 \times 0.5 = 50\%$.

The probability of genotype PP is 0%. Half of their offspring are Pp and exhibit a purple flower phenotype, and half are pp and exhibit a white flower phenotype.

Its offspring with the white plant determine the purple plant genotype.

If the offspring are purple, the unknown parent must be genotype PP.

If the offspring is half purple, half white, the unknown parent must be genotype Pp.

Testcross, Punnett square and observed phenotypes

This test cross (homozygous recessive with unknown genotype) is summarized:

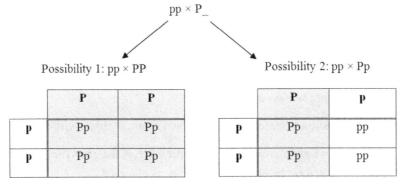

100% purple offspring indicated a purple a homozygous parent

50% purple offspring, and 50% white offspring indicates a purple parent that is heterozygous

Two-trait test cross and backcross

For a two-trait test cross (e.g., seed color), the results are an extension of the single trait test cross.

If a double homozygous recessive parent (rryy) is crossed with a round-seeded yellow parent of an unknown genotype, the unknown parent has four possible genotypes: RRYY, RrYY, RRYy, RrYy.

Known parent genotype	Possible parent genotype	Possible parent gametes	Offspring phenotype ratio
rryy	RRYY	RY, RY, RY, RY	1 round yellow
rryy	RrYY	RY, RY, rY, rY	1 round yellow : 1 wrinkled yellow
rryy	RRYy	RY, RY, Ry, Ry	1 round yellow : 1 round green
rryy	RrYy	RY, rY, Ry, ry	1 round yellow : 1 wrinkled yellow : 1 round green : 1 wrinkled green

After creating hybrid F1 individuals from a parental generation, a *backcross* is performed by breeding the offspring with the parents (or an individual with the same genotype as the parents).

This conserves desirable traits in the F2.

Backcrosses are used for a "knock out" (i.e., inactivate the gene) to study the function of a specific gene.

Backcrossing occurs naturally in small populations, especially among plants.

Artificial backcrossing is done in genetic research to study the function of specific genes by eliminating them and observing the effect when absent.

Gene mapping, crossover frequencies and map units

The rate of "unlinking" of genes maps the *physical distances* between two genes on the same chromosome.

The further apart two genes are, the more likely they become unlinked during crossing over.

The frequency of recombination is an estimate of linkage because it indicates the distance between loci.

The maximum frequency of recombination is 50%. For example, genes undergoing recombination 50% of the time are unlinked.

Genes undergoing recombination 10% of the time must be close as it is difficult for them to be separated.

Frequencies are calculated by dividing the number of recombinant offspring by the number of offspring.

Recombinants are identified by their rarity amongst offspring since parental-type offspring are frequent.

If more than two genes are studied, different types of crossing over can occur, and the recombinants are divided into two-, three-, or four-stranded crossovers.

Two-stranded crossovers occur more frequently than three-stranded crossovers; four-stranded crossovers are rarest.

A 1% recombination frequency equals 1 map unit, measured in *centimorgans* (cM) as an arbitrary, relative unit and not physical distances.

Suppose crosses are performed for three genes, and recombination frequencies are calculated.

The genes can be ordered (arrange by relative distance) since one map relationship explains the distances between them.

Biochemical methods map the physical distances between loci by the number of DNA nucleotide bases.

Human chromosomes must be mapped this way since it is impossible to measure recombination frequency among a person's offspring due to the small sample size and lack of control over reproduction.

Biometry and statistical methods in genetics

Mendel's knowledge of statistics, a new branch of mathematics at the time, greatly aided his work.

Today, statistics is an integral field of life sciences.

Biometry, or *biostatistics,* applies mathematical models and statistics to a vast array of biological fields.

Biometry is used for biological experiments, the collection, summarization, analysis of data, and interpretation of and inferences from the data.

Problem-solving in genetics usually relies on statistics.

Allelic, genotypic, and phenotypic frequencies are calculated using statistics to determine the characteristics of a family (or population).

Models are applied that describe genetic inheritance, even for complex non-Mendelian patterns.

Notes for active learning

Notes for active learning

PRACTICE QUESTIONS

&

DETAILED EXPLANATIONS

Practice Questions: DNA, Protein Synthesis & Gene Expression

1. DNA and RNA differ because:

A. only DNA contains phosphodiester bonds

B. only RNA contains pyrimidines

C. DNA is in the nucleus, and RNA is in the cytosol

D. RNA is associated with ribosomes, and DNA is associated with histones

E. RNA contains a phosphate group in its ribose ring

2. In the 1920s, circumstantial evidence indicated that DNA was the genetic material. Which experiments led to the acceptance of this hypothesis?

A. Griffith's experiments with *Streptococcus pneumoniae*

B. Avery, MacLeod and McCarty's work with isolating the transforming principle

C. Hershey and Chase's experiments with viruses and radioisotopes

D. A, B and C were used to support this hypothesis

E. Darwin's theory of natural selection

3. The N-glycosidic bond is relatively unstable within a guanine molecule and can be hydrolyzed through depurination. Which molecule is likely to undergo depurination?

A. sterols

B. lipids

C. phospholipids

D. proteins

E. DNA

4. What process duplicates a single gene?

A. Unequal recombination at repeated sequences that flank the gene

B. Equal recombination at repeated sequences that flank the gene

C. Unequal recombination within a single gene

D. Equal recombination within a single gene

E. All the above

5. Which element is NOT within nucleic acids?

A. nitrogen

B. oxygen

C. phosphorus

D. sulfur

E. carbon

6. Which RNA molecule is translated?

A. miRNA

B. tRNA

C. rRNA

D. mRNA

E. C and D

7. The aging of normal cells is associated with:

A. loss of telomerase activity

B. a decrease in contact inhibition promoting factor

C. an increase in mutation rate

D. activation of the maturation-

E. extranuclear inheritance

8. Protein synthesis in eukaryotic cells initiates in which structures?

A. nucleus

B. Golgi

C. cytoplasm

D. rough endoplasmic reticulum

E. smooth endoplasmic reticulum

9. When a gene is duplicated on one chromatid, the gene on the other chromatid is:

A. duplicated

B. inverted

C. transposed to another site

D. maintained as a single gene

E. deleted

10. Experiments designed by Avery, McLeod, and McCarty to identify the transforming principle were based on:

I. purifying each of the macromolecule types from a cell-free extract

II. removing each of the macromolecules from a cell, then testing its type

III. selectively destroying the different macromolecules in a cell-free extract

A. I only

B. II only

C. III only

D. I, II and III

E. I and II only

11. What is the term for a blotting method where proteins are transferred from a gel to membranes and probed by antibodies to specific proteins?

A. Eastern blotting

B. Western blotting

C. Northern blotting

D. Southern blotting

E. both Northern and Western blotting

12. The figure shows a nucleotide. At what position will the incoming nucleotide be attached in the figure?

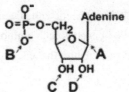

A. position A

B. position B

C. position C

D. position D

E. none of the above

13. All are correct about DNA, EXCEPT:

A. the strands are anti-parallel

B. the basic unit is nucleotide

C. the sugar molecule is deoxyribose

D. guanine binds to cytosine via three hydrogen bonds

E. adenine and guanine are pyrimidines

14. Tumor-suppressor genes normally control:

A. cell differentiation

B. necrosis

C. cell proliferation or activation of apoptosis

D. sister chromatid separation

E. protein degradation

15. Select the correct statement for aminoacyl tRNA synthetase.

A. It binds several different amino acids

B. It is an enzyme that uses energy from ATP to attach a specific amino acid to a tRNA

C. It is a tRNA that covalently binds amino acids

D. It synthesizes tRNA

E. It synthesizes rRNA

16. Griffith's experiment with pneumococcus demonstrated that:

A. smooth bacteria can survive heating

B. DNA, not protein, is the genetic molecule

C. materials from dead organisms can affect and change living organisms

D. nonliving viruses can change living cells

E. the virus injects its DNA into the host cell

17. The genetic code deciphered by Noble laureate Marshall W. Nirenberg (1927-2020) in 1964 encodes each amino acid by three nucleotides (codons). How many possible codons exist in nature that encode 20 amino acids in polypeptides?

A. 4   **C.** 27

B. 20   **D.** 64

                                                      E. 16

18. What mechanism targets proteins to organelles (e.g., chloroplast, mitochondrion)?

A. Addition of phosphate groups to the protein

B. Synthesizing the proteins as zymogens

C. Adding prosthetic groups to the protein

D. Cysteine bond formation

E. The signal sequence at the N-terminus of the polypeptide

19. When DNA is treated with 2-aminopurine, adenine is replaced by guanine on one strand. During replication, the complementary strand will have a substitution of:

A. guanine for adenine   **C.** cytosine for thymine

B. adenine for guanine   **D.** thymine for cytosine

                                                      E. adenine for cytosine

20. Before Nobel laureate Marshall W. Nirenberg *et al.* in 1964 determined the genetic code experimentally, why was it hypothesized that each codon would contain at least three bases?

A. Three bases are needed to produce a stable codon structure

B. There were three known nucleotide bases

C. There were more proteins than nucleotide bases

D. Three bases can form $4^3 = 64$ pairs, which is enough to encode 20 amino acids

E. There were twenty known amino acids

21. DNA of bacteria grown in a heavy (^{15}N) medium was isolated and added to an *in vitro* synthesis system. Then the bacteria are grown in a light (^{14}N) medium. After several hours, a sample of DNA was taken and analyzed for differing densities. How many DNA densities were in the sample after 2 generations?

A. 1   **C.** 4

B. 2   **D.** 8

                                                      E. 12

22. Which experimental procedure(s) simultaneously measure(s) the level of all mRNAs in a tissue?

      I. Northern blot   II. *In situ* hybridization   III. Microarray experiment

- **A.** I only
- **B.** II only

- **C.** III only
- **D.** I, II and III
- **E.** I and III only

23. To demonstrate that DNA is the "transforming principle," Avery, MacLeod, and McCarty showed that DNA could transform nonvirulent strains of pneumococcus. Their hypothesis was strengthened by their demonstration:

- **A.** enzymes that destroyed proteins destroyed transforming activity
- **B.** enzymes that destroyed nucleic acids destroyed transforming activity
- **C.** enzymes that destroyed complex carbohydrates destroyed transforming activity
- **D.** the transforming activity was destroyed by boiling
- **E.** other strains of bacteria were transformed successfully

24. Which components of codon-anticodon hybridization on ribosomes determine the fidelity of protein synthesis?

- **A.** mRNA & tRNA
- **B.** mRNA & rRNA

- **C.** tRNA & rRNA
- **D.** DNA & RNA polymerase
- **E.** RNA polymerase

25. Which procedure measures mRNA levels from only a single gene?

      I. Northern blot   II. *In situ* hybridization   III. Microarray experiment

- **A.** II only
- **B.** I and II only

- **C.** II and III only
- **D.** I, II and III
- **E.** I and III only

26. Which stage of cell division is the stage when chromosomes replicate?

- **A.** prophase
- **B.** telophase

- **C.** anaphase
- **D.** metaphase
- **E.** interphase

27. If the transcript's sequence is 5'-CUAAGGGCUAC-3', what is the sequence of the DNA template?

A. 3'-GUAGCCCUUAG-5'

B. 3'-GTACGCCTTAG-5'

C. 5'-GTAACCCTTAG-3'

D. 5'-GUTACCUGUAG-3'

E. 5'-GTAGCCCTTAG-3'

28. Duplicated genes:

A. are more common in prokaryote genomes than in eukaryote genomes

B. are closely related but diverged in sequence and function over evolutionary time

C. never encodes for essential proteins, such as transcription factors

D. encode for proteins that catalyze different steps of a biochemical pathway

E. all the above

29. The Hershey–Chase experiment:

A. proved that DNA replication is semiconservative

B. used ^{32}P to label protein

C. used ^{35}S to label DNA

D. supported the hypothesis that DNA is the transforming molecule

E. both A and C

30. Which statement is NOT correct about DNA replication?

A. DNA polymerase synthesizes and proofreads the DNA

B. RNA primers are necessary for the hybridization of the polymerase

C. Ligase relaxes positive supercoils that accumulate as the replication fork opens

D. DNA polymerase adds Okazaki fragments in a 5' → 3' direction

E. DNA polymerase adds deoxynucleotides in a 5' → 3' direction

31. Which structures represent a peptide bond between adjacent amino acids?

A. structure A

B. structure B

C. structure C

D. structure D

E. structures A and D

32. All these statements apply to proteins, EXCEPT:

A. they regulate cell membrane trafficking
B. they catalyze chemical reactions
C. they can be hormones
D. they undergo self-replication
E. they bind antigens

33. Eukaryote RNA polymerase usually:

A. binds to the TATAA promoter sequence and initiates transcription
B. needs general transcription factors to bind to the promoter and initiate basal-level transcription
C. needs specific regulatory transcription factors to bind to the promoter and initiate basal-level transcription
D. transcribes tRNA genes
E. transcribes mRNA genes

34. If an RNA sequence has a cytosine content of 25%, what is its adenine content?

A. 50%
B. 37.5%
C. 12.5%
D. 25%
E. cannot be determined

35. If a portion of prokaryotic mRNA has the base sequence 5′-ACUACUAUGCGUCGA-3′, what could result from a mutation where the underlined base is changed to A?

    I. truncation of the polypeptide
    II. inhibition of initiation of translation
    III. no effect on protein synthesis

A. I and II only
B. I and III only
C. II and III only
D. III only
E. II only

36. Which statement is INCORRECT about the genetic code?

A. Many amino acids are specified by more than one codon
B. Most codons specify more than one amino acid
C. There are multiple stop codons
D. Codons are 3 bases in length
E. The start codon inserts methionine at the amino end of the polypeptide

37. In bacteria, the enzyme that removes the RNA primers is:

A. DNA ligase

B. primase

C. reverse transcriptase

D. DNA polymerase I

E. helicase

38. Okazaki fragments are:

A. synthesized in a 5'→ 3' direction by DNA polymerase I

B. covalently linked by DNA polymerase I

C. components of the leading strand

D. components of DNA synthesized to fill in gaps after excision of the RNA primer

E. synthesized in a 5'→ 3' direction by DNA polymerase III

39. Peptide bond synthesis is catalyzed by:

A. tRNA in the cytoplasm

B. ribosomal proteins

C. ribosomal RNA

D. mRNA in the ribosome

E. none of the above

40. Which statement does NOT apply to protein synthesis?

A. The process does not require energy

B. rRNA is required for proper binding of the mRNA message

C. tRNA molecules shuttle amino acids assembled into polypeptides

D. The amino acid is bound to the 3' end of the tRNA

E. The mRNA is synthesized from 5' → 3'

41. All statements about PCR are correct, EXCEPT:

A. PCR can be used to obtain large quantities of a particular DNA sequence

B. PCR does not require knowledge of the terminal DNA sequences of the region to be amplified

C. PCR uses a DNA polymerase to synthesize DNA

D. PCR uses short synthetic oligonucleotide primers

E. PCR involves heating the DNA sample to denature complementary base pairing

42. The shape of a tRNA is determined primarily by:

   A. its number of bases

   B. proteins that bind it

   C. tRNA and aminoacyl tRNA synthetase interactions

   D. intramolecular base pairing

   E. hydrophobic interactions

43. In prokaryotic cells, methylated guanine contributes to:

   A. increased rate of DNA replication

   B. decreased rate of DNA replication

   C. correcting the separation of DNA strands

   D. proofreading the replicated strands

   E. correcting mismatched pairs of bases

44. In the polymerization reaction by DNA polymerase, what is the function of magnesium?

$$\text{Mg+2, 4 dNTPs, DNA polymerase}$$

Primer (free 3' OH) + 5' PPP $\longrightarrow$ Primer 3'O-P-5' + PPi

   A. cofactor   **C.** substrate

   B. monovalent metal ion   **D.** enzyme

                                          E. coenzyme

45. The structure of the ribosome is created by:

   I. internal base pairing of rRNA   III. internal base pairing of mRNA

   II. ribosomal proteins   IV. internal base pairing of tRNA

   A. I only   **C.** I and II only

   B. II only   **D.** I, II and IV only

                                           E. I, II and III only

46. Which statement is true for tRNA?

   A. It has some short double-stranded segments

   B. It has a poly-A tail

   C. It is produced in the nucleolus

   D. It is a long molecule of RNA

   E. It is the template for protein synthesis

47. Which chemical group is at the 5' end of a single polynucleotide strand?

A. diester group

B. purine base

C. hydroxyl group

D. phosphate group

E. nitrogen group

48. The drug aminoacyl-tRNA is an analog of puromycin. Both have an amino group capable of forming a peptide bond, but puromycin lacks a carboxyl group to form another peptide bond. What is the possible effect of adding puromycin to bacteria undergoing protein synthesis?

A. Inhibition of initiation of protein synthesis

B. Inhibition of entry of aminoacyl-tRNA into the P site during elongation

C. Inability to form a complete ribosome

D. Substitution of puromycin for another amino acid in the protein, yielding a normal-length protein

E. Termination of protein synthesis via covalent attachment of puromycin

49. In *E. coli* cells, DNA polymerase I:

    I.   synthesizes most of the Okazaki fragments

    II. simultaneously copies both strands of DNA

    III. degrades the RNA primer portion of Okazaki fragments

A. I only

B. II only

C. III only

D. I and III only

E. I and II only

50. During DNA synthesis, the error rate is on the order of one mismatched nucleotide per:

A. 100

B. 1,000

C. 10,000

D. 1,000,000

E. 10,000,000

51. All are contained within a molecule of DNA, EXCEPT:

A. nitrogenous bases

B. phosphodiester bonds

C. polypeptide bonds

D. deoxyribose sugars

E. phosphate groups

52. In *E. coli* cells, DNA polymerase III:

    A. synthesizes most of the Okazaki fragments

    B. removes the RNA primer

    C. is the only DNA polymerase used by *E. coli* during replication

    D. degrades the RNA portion of an Okazaki fragment

    E. synthesizes DNA in the 3' to 5' direction

53. Which molecule belongs to a different chemical category than the others?

    A. uracil   **C.** adenine

    B. guanine   **D.** thymine

                                               E. cysteine

54. The enzyme that cleaves DNA at the sequence-specific site is:

    A. restriction endonuclease   **C.** DNA polymerase

    B. exonuclease   **D.** ligase

                                               E. integrase

55. *E. coli* RNA polymerase-initiated transcription and synthesized one phosphodiester bond. Which molecule shown is RNA polymerase made from?

56. What rate does PCR increase the amount of DNA during each cycle?

   A. additively

   B. exponentially

   C. linearly

   D. systematically

   E. gradually

57. Which is present in RNA but absent in DNA?

   A. additional hydroxyl group

   B. hydrogen bonds

   C. thymine

   D. double helix

   E. phosphodiester bonds

58. After DNA strands are synthesized, which enzyme completes the process of DNA replication?

   A. primase

   B. ligase

   C. helicase

   D. reverse transcriptase

   E. both B and D

59. When a base is paired with its complementary strand, which strand would have the highest melting point?

   A. TTAGTCTC

   B. TTTTAAAA

   C. AGCTTCGT

   D. CGCGTATA

   E. GCCAGTCG

60. A technique that investigates gene function by mutating wildtype genes is:

   A. contig building

   B. transgenetics

   C. reverse genetics

   D. gene therapy

   E. gene mapping

61. How many high-energy phosphate bonds are needed to translate a 50-amino acid polypeptide (starting with mRNA, tRNA, amino acids, and the necessary enzymes)?

   A. 49

   B. 50

   C. 101

   D. 199

   E. 150

62. The mRNA in *E. coli* cells is composed primarily of:

    A. four bases – A, T, C, G

    B. phosphodiester linkages connecting deoxyribonucleotide molecules

    C. two strands that base pair in an anti-parallel orientation

    D. processed RNA molecule containing introns

    E. phosphodiester linkages connecting ribonucleotide molecules

63. Which statement about DNA mismatch repair is correct?

    A. DNA is scanned for any base-pairing mismatches after methyl groups are added to guanines

    B. Errors in replication made by DNA polymerase are corrected on the unmethylated strand

    C. The proofreading mechanism removes all abnormal bases

    D. Repairs from high-energy radiation damage are made

    E. Mismatch repair occurs on each strand of DNA during replication

64. What is the first amino acid of each protein of eukaryotic cells?

    A. methionine   **C.** valine

    B. glutamate   **D.** proline

                                 E. isoleucine

65. DNA in *E. coli* is composed of:

    I. four bases – A, T, C, G

    II. phosphodiester linkages that connect deoxyribonucleotide molecules

    III. two strands that base pair in an anti-parallel orientation

    IV. phosphodiester linkages that utilize the 3'-OH

    A. I and II only   **C.** I, II and III only

    B. I and III only   **D.** I, II, III and IV

                                   E. II, III and IV only

66. If a peptide has the sequence val-ser-met-pro and the tRNA molecules used in its synthesis have the corresponding sequence of anticodons 3'-CAG-5', 3'-UCG-5', 3'-UAC-5', 3'-UUU-5', what sequence of the DNA codes for this peptide?

    A. 5'–CAGTCGTACTTT–3'   **C.** 5'–GACGCTCATTTT–3'

    B. 5'–TTTCATGCTGAC–3'   **D.** 5'–UUUCAUGCUGAC–3'

                                   E. 5'–CAGUCGUACUUU–3'

67. The site of the DNA template that RNA polymerase binds to during transcription is:

A. promoter

B. leader sequence

C. enhancer

D. domain

E. transcription factor

68. Which dipeptide is synthesized by a ribosome?

A. isoleucine-glycine

B. cytosine-guanine

C. proline-thymine

D. uracil-glutamic acid

E. isoleucine-glycine and uracil-glutamic acid

69. Which is the correct order of events in delivering a protein to its cellular destination?

A. Signal sequence binds to docking protein → transmembrane-gated channel opens → protein enters the organelle

B. Membrane channel is formed → signal sequence binds to docking protein → chaperonins unfold protein → protein enters the organelle → protein refolds

C. Chaperonins unfold protein → signal sequence binds to docking protein → membrane channel is formed → protein enters the organelle → protein refolds

D. Membrane channel is formed → chaperonins unfold protein → signal sequence binds to docking protein → protein enters the organelle → protein refolds

E. Signal sequence binds to docking protein → membrane channel is formed → chaperonins unfold protein → protein enters the organelle → protein refolds

70. Select the correct mRNA sequences depending on the direction RNA polymerase transcribes.

RNA sequence if RNA polymerase goes left: RNA sequence if RNA polymerase goes right:

Left ← → Right

3' ——— C C C | A A A ——— 5'
        G G G | T T T
5' ——————————————— 3'

RNA polymerase

A. 5'-GGG-3' 5'-AAA-3'

B. 5'-GGG-3' 5'-UUU-3'

C. 5'-CCC-3' 5'-AAA-3'

D. 5'-CCC-3' 5'-UUU-3'

E. None of the above

71. Which statement is TRUE for the base composition of DNA?

   A. In double-stranded DNA, the number of G bases equals the number of T bases
   B. In double-stranded DNA, the number of A bases equals the number of T bases
   C. In double-stranded DNA, the number of C bases equals the number of T bases
   D. In every single strand, the number of A bases equals the number of T bases
   E. In double-stranded DNA, the number of G bases equals the number of A bases

72. The figure shows a replication fork in *E. coli*.
Which of the indicated sites is the 3' end of the lagging
strand?

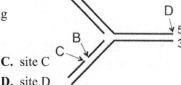

   A. site A   **C.** site C
   B. site B   **D.** site D
                          E. sites C and D

73. Ribosomal subunits are isolated from bacteria grown in a "heavy" ^{13}C and ^{15}N medium and added to an *in vitro* system that actively synthesizes protein. Following translation, a sample is removed and centrifuged. Which would be the best illustration of centrifugation results?

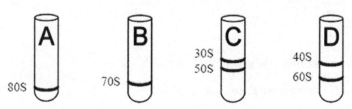

   A. Test tube A   **C.** Test tube C
   B. Test tube B   **D.** Test tube D
                               E. Test tubes A and C

74. Which statement is TRUE?

   A. polypeptides are synthesized by the addition of amino acids to the amino terminus
   B. prokaryotic RNA usually undergoes nuclear processing
   C. RNA polymerase has a proof-reading activity
   D. prokaryotic RNA contains introns
   E. 3' end of mRNA corresponds to the carboxyl terminus of the protein

169

75. A codon for histidine is 5'-CAU-3'. The anticodon in the tRNA that brings histidine to the ribosome is:

A. 5'-CAU-3'   **C.** 5'-UAC-3'

B. 5'-GUA-3'   **D.** 5'-AUG-3'

                                           E. none of the above

76. During translation elongation, the existing polypeptide chain is transferred to which site as the ribosome moves in the 3' direction?

A. tRNA occupying the A site   **C.** ribosomal rRNA

B. tRNA occupying the P site   **D.** signal recognition particle

                                           E. none of the above

77. Which primer will amplify the following DNA fragments *via* PCR?

     5'-ATCGGTATGTAACGCTCACCTGT-3'

A. 5'-ACAG-3'   **C.** 5'-TAGC-3'

B. 5'-AGAC-3'   **D.** 5'-GACT-3'

                                           E. 5'-CTGT-3'

78. Which statement about the genetic code is FALSE?

A. It is mostly the same for *E. coli* and humans

B. It is redundant

C. It is ambiguous

D. It has one codon for starting translation

E. All the above are true

79. What portion of the polypeptide chain is responsible for establishing and maintaining the force used to stabilize the secondary structure?

A. C-terminus   **C.** carbonyl oxygen

B. N-terminus   **D.** R-groups

                                           E. both A and B

		U	C	A	G	
				Second base		
First base (5' end)	U	UUU ⎤ Phe UUC ⎦ UUA ⎤ Leu UUG ⎦	UCU ⎤ UCC ⎥ Ser UCA ⎥ UCG ⎦	UAU ⎤ Tyr UAC ⎦ UAA Stop UAG Stop	UGU ⎤ Cys UGC ⎦ UGA Stop UGG Trp	U C A G
	C	CUU ⎤ CUC ⎥ Leu CUA ⎥ CUG ⎦	CCU ⎤ CCC ⎥ Pro CCA ⎥ CCG ⎦	CAU ⎤ His CAC ⎦ CAA ⎤ Gln CAG ⎦	CGU ⎤ CGC ⎥ Arg CGA ⎥ CGG ⎦	U C A G
	A	AUU ⎤ AUC ⎥ Ile AUA ⎦ AUG Met start	ACU ⎤ ACC ⎥ Thr ACA ⎥ ACG ⎦	AAU ⎤ Asn AAC ⎦ AAA ⎤ Lys AAG ⎦	AGU ⎤ Ser AGC ⎦ AGA ⎤ Arg AGG ⎦	U C A G
	G	GUU ⎤ GUC ⎥ Val GUA ⎥ GUG ⎦	GCU ⎤ GCC ⎥ Ala GCA ⎥ GCG ⎦	GAU ⎤ Asp GAC ⎦ GAA ⎤ Glu GAG ⎦	GGU ⎤ GGC ⎥ Gly GGA ⎥ GGG ⎦	U C A G

80. A ribosome has made a tripeptide, MET-ARG-SER, attached to the tRNA in the P site. Using the genetic code table, what codon is in the E site of the ribosome?

A. AUG

B. CGU

C. UCA

D. UGA

E. It cannot be determined

81. A ribosome has made a tripeptide, MET-ARG-SER, attached to the tRNA in the P site. Using the genetic code table, what codon is in the A site of the ribosome?

A. AUG

B. CGU

C. UCA

D. UGA

E. It cannot be determined

82. Which is an example of a transversion mutation where purine gets converted to pyrimidine?

A. uracil → thymine

B. cytosine → thymine

C. thymine → adenine

D. guanine → adenine

E. guanine → cytosine

83. Recombinant DNA experiments utilize plasmids because:

    A. they contain foreign DNA

    B. their genetic material cannot be cut with restriction enzymes

    C. they are unable to replicate inside the bacteria

    D. they are used to transform bacteria

    E. they are a natural part of the bacterial genome

84. Which task requires recombinant DNA technology?

    A. Creating bacteria that produce human growth hormone

    B. Creating a polyploid cherry tree

    C. Crossing two types of orange trees to create new orange fruits

    D. Crossing a donkey with a horse to breed a mule

    E. Paternity testing

85. Gene therapy is successful when:

    A. the person's cells express the newly introduced gene

    B. the replacement gene is integrated into viral DNA

    C. the virus with the replacement gene enters the person's cells

    D. the person's cells replicate the newly introduced gene

    E. the replacement gene is integrated into the person's genome

Notes or active learning

Notes or active learning

Detailed Explanations: DNA, Protein Synthesis & Gene Expression

Answer Key

1: D	11: B	21: B	31: A	41: B	51: C	61: D	71: B	81: E
2: D	12: C	22: C	32: D	42: D	52: A	62: E	72: B	82: E
3: E	13: E	23: B	33: B	43: E	53: E	63: B	73: C	83: D
4: A	14: C	24: A	34: E	44: A	54: A	64: A	74: E	84: A
5: D	15: B	25: B	35: A	45: C	55: C	65: D	75: D	85: A
6: D	16: C	26: E	36: B	46: A	56: B	66: B	76: B	
7: A	17: D	27: E	37: D	47: D	57: A	67: A	77: A	
8: C	18: E	28: B	38: E	48: E	58: B	68: A	78: C	
9: E	19: C	29: D	39: C	49: C	59: E	69: E	79: C	
10: C	20: D	30: C	40: A	50: D	60: C	70: D	80: B	

1. D is correct.

Histones are basic (i.e., positively charged) proteins associated with nuclei DNA to condense chromatin.

Nuclear DNA does not appear in free linear strands; instead, it is highly condensed and wrapped around histones (i.e., positively-charged proteins) to fit inside the nucleus and form chromosomes.

Three major types of RNA engage in gene expression:

1) *messenger* RNA (mRNA) molecules carry the coding sequences (i.e., "blueprints") for protein synthesis and are transcripts;

2) *ribosomal* RNA (rRNA) forms the core of a cell's ribosomes (i.e., macromolecular cellular particles where protein synthesis takes place);

3) *transfer* RNA (tRNA) molecules transport amino acids (i.e., protein building blocks) to the ribosomes during protein synthesis.

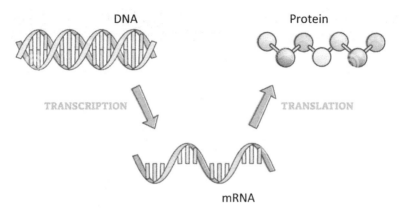

Gene expression with DNA transcribed into mRNA, which is
translated into protein

2. D is correct.

Frederick Griffith (1928) reported an early experiment suggesting that bacteria transfer genetic information through *transformation*.

Griffith observed a *transforming principle*, where heat-killed S (smooth) bacteria was destroyed, and (now known) its DNA survived the process and was incorporated by R (rough) strain bacteria.

S genetic fragments protected R strain bacteria from host immunity and killed the host.

3. E is correct.

Depurination is the hydrolysis of the glycosidic bond of DNA and RNA purine nucleotides guanine or adenine.

Nucleotides have sugar, phosphate, and base (A, C, G, T or U).

For DNA, the sugar is deoxyribose, while RNA contains ribose.

Glycosidic bonds are hemiacetal groups of a saccharide (or an amino acid) and the hydroxyl group of an organic compound (e.g., alcohol).

Glycosidic bond formation from the nucleophilic attack of alcohol on the anomeric carbon of
a hemiacetal

4. A is correct.

Unequal crossing over is a gene duplication (or deletion) event that deletes a sequence in one strand of the chromatid. It replaces it with duplication from its sister chromatid in mitosis, or homologous chromosomes recombine during prophase I in meiosis.

5. D is correct.

Sulfur is in the amino acid cysteine but is absent in nucleic acids.

Hershey-Chase (i.e., associate *blender*) experiment in 1952 used radiolabeled molecules of phosphorus (^{32}P for nucleic acids) and sulfur (^{35}S for proteins) to determine whether nucleic acids (phosphorus) or protein (sulfur) carried the genetic information.

Nucleic acids contain C, H, O, N and P and are polymers of *nucleotide* subunits.

Nucleic acids (e.g., DNA, RNA) encode cellular information for protein synthesis and replication.

6. D is correct.

mRNA is the subclass of RNAs molecule translated into proteins.

7. A is correct.

Aging of normal cells is associated with a loss of *telomerase activity*.

8. C is correct.

Translation is initiated on ribosomes within the cytoplasm.

A: *transcription* (not translation) occurs in the nucleus.

B: *Golgi* receives proteins from the rough endoplasmic reticulum for processing and sorting.

Golgi modifies (e.g., adds carbohydrate groups) and sorts proteins in the *secretory pathway*.

D: proteins destined for the *lumen of the rough endoplasmic reticulum* have at their amino terminus a particular sequence of amino acids referred to as a *leader sequence* (about 6 to 10 amino acids).

Signal recognition protein (SRP) recognizes the leader sequence and binds a receptor on the rough ER, attaching the ribosome and the nascent polypeptide to the endoplasmic reticulum (ER) membrane.

9. E is correct.

When a gene is duplicated by crossing over between chromatids, the gene on the other chromatid is deleted.

Unequal crossing over is a gene duplication (or deletion) event that deletes a sequence in one strand of the chromatid. It replaces it with duplication from its sister chromatid in mitosis, or homologous chromosomes recombine during prophase I in meiosis.

10. C is correct.

To show that DNA, not RNA, protein, or other cell components, was responsible for transformation, Avery, MacLeod, and McCarty (1944) used several biochemical tests.

Trypsin, chymotrypsin, and ribonuclease (enzymes digesting proteins or RNA) did not affect the transforming agent causing the disease.

DNase treatment degrades DNA and destroys the extract's ability to cause disease.

Streptococcus pneumoniae (i.e., pneumococcus) is a Gram-positive pathogenic bacterium.

S. pneumoniae was recognized as a major cause of pneumonia in the late 19th century and has been the subject of numerous humoral immunity (i.e., antibody-mediated) studies.

11. B is correct.

Western blotting separates proteins by electrophoresis and is commonly used to identify the presence of HIV antibodies (proteins).

Blotting techniques rely on gel electrophoresis to separate DNA, RNA, or proteins based on size.

After resolution (separation) by electrophoresis, the gel (containing resolved products) is blotted (i.e., transferred to nitrocellulose).

After transferring the macromolecules (DNA, RNA, or proteins) from the gel to the blotting paper by capillary action, the blotting paper is probed by specific markers that hybridize with complementary sequences fixed on the blotting paper.

A: *Eastern blotting* does not exist.

C: *Northern blotting* uses RNA in gel electrophoresis.

D: *Southern blotting* uses DNA in gel electrophoresis.

12. C is correct.

Position C represents the ribose sugar's 3' hydroxyl (~OH).

As in DNA, *the 3' hydroxyl is the site of attachment*.

RNA and DNA require a free 3' OH for the nucleic acid to increase length.

Position D contains a 2' hydroxyl (~OH) that distinguishes this sugar as ribose, as opposed to DNA which would lack the 2' hydroxyl (deoxyribose = without oxygen) at the 2' position of the sugar.

13. E is correct.

Adenine and guanine are *purines*.

Cytosine and thymine/uracil are *pyrimidines*; note the presence of *y* for pyrimidines.

A: DNA strands are *antiparallel*: one strand has a 5'→ 3' polarity, and its complementary strand 3' → 5'.

B: DNA consists of nucleotides, which have a phosphate group, a deoxyribose sugar, and a base (A, C, G, T).

D: cytosine binds guanine with three hydrogen bonds.

Adenine binds thymine (in DNA) or uracil (in RNA) with two hydrogen bonds.

14. C is correct.

Tumor suppressor gene protects a cell from aberrant cell cycles.

When this gene mutates to cause a loss (or reduction) in its function, the cell can progress to cancer, usually with other genetic changes.

The loss of *tumor suppressor genes* may be more important than *proto-oncogene* activation for forming many types of human cancer cells.

Apoptosis is the process of programmed cell death (PCD) that may occur in multicellular organisms.

Biochemical events lead to characteristic cell changes (morphology) and death, including blebbing, cell shrinkage, nuclear fragmentation, chromatin condensation, and chromosomal DNA fragmentation.

In contrast to necrosis (i.e., traumatic cell death that results from acute cellular injury), apoptosis confers advantages during an organism's lifecycle.

For example, a human embryo separates fingers and toes because cells between the digits undergo *apoptosis*.

Unlike necrosis, apoptosis produces cell fragments called *apoptotic bodies* that phagocytic cells can engulf and quickly remove before the cell contents spill onto surrounding cells and cause damage.

A: *telomerase* is an enzyme that adds DNA sequence repeats (i.e., TTAGGG) to the 3' end of DNA strands in the telomere regions at the ends of eukaryotic chromosomes.

This region of repeated nucleotides as telomeres with noncoding DNA hinders the loss of essential DNA from chromosome ends. When the chromosome is copied, 100–200 nucleotides are lost, causing no damage to the coding region of the DNA.

Telomerase is a reverse transcriptase that carries its RNA molecule used as a template when it elongates telomeres that have been shortened after each replication cycle.

Embryonic stem cells express telomerase, allowing them to divide repeatedly.

In adults, telomerase is highly expressed in cells that divide regularly (e.g., male germ cells, lymphocytes, and specific adult stem cells). Telomerase is not expressed in most adult somatic cells.

15. B is correct.

Aminoacyl tRNA synthetase (enzyme) uses energy from ATP to attach a specific amino acid to tRNA.

16. C is correct.

DNA was the transforming principle verified in experiments by Avery, MacLeod, and McCarty (1944) and Hershey and Chase (1952).

17. D is correct.

There are 4 different nucleotides (adenine, cytosine, guanine, and thymine/uracil).

Each codon is composed of 3 nucleotides.

Therefore, there must be 64 (4^3) possible variations of codons to encode for the 20 amino acids.

Genetic code is *degenerate* (i.e., redundant) because several codons encode for the same amino acid.

61 codons encode for amino acids and 3 stop codons that terminate translation.

18. E is correct.

Signal sequence at the N-terminus of the polypeptide targets proteins to organelles (e.g., chloroplast, mitochondrion).

19. C is correct.

Adenine pairs with thymine *via* 2 hydrogen bonds, while guanine pairs with cytosine *via* 3 hydrogen bonds.

Treatment of DNA with 2-aminopurine causes the adenine-thymine (A-T) base pair to be replaced with a guanine-thymine (G-T) base pair (before replication).

Thymine is replaced by cytosine: G-C base pair after replication.

This single-point mutation is incorporated into future generations.

If the mutation had been corrected before replication (via proofreading mechanisms during replication), there would be no change in the DNA base sequence.

20. D is correct.

Codons with two bases would be insufficient because the four bases in a two-base codon would form $4^2 = 16$ pairs, less than the 20 combinations needed to specify the amino acids.

A triplet is sufficient because four bases in a three-base codon can form $4^3 = 64$ pairs, enough to encode the 20 amino acids.

21. B is correct.

After one replication, the DNA was at an intermediate density between ^{14}N and ^{15}N.

After two replications, there were two densities – one band in the centrifuge tube was an intermediate between the ^{14}N and ^{15}N, while the other consisted of ^{14}N.

The *semiconservative* DNA replication model was one of three tested by the Meselson-Stahl (1958) experiment.

> **Semiconservative replication** would produce two copies containing one original and one new strand.

> **Conservative replication** would leave the two original template DNA strands in a double helix and produce a copy composed of two new strands containing the new DNA base pairs.

> **Dispersive replication** would produce two copies of the DNA, each containing distinct regions of DNA composed of either original or new strands.

In the Meselson-Stahl (1957-58) experiments, *E. coli* were grown for several generations in a medium with ^{15}N.

When DNA was extracted and separated by centrifugation, the DNA separated according to density.

The E. coli cells with ^{15}N in their DNA were transferred to a ^{14}N medium and divided.

The DNA of the cells grown in a ^{15}N medium had a higher density than cells grown in a standard ^{14}N medium.

Since *conservative replication* would result in equal amounts of DNA of the higher and lower densities (but no intermediate density), conservative replication was excluded.

This result was consistent with *semiconservative* and *dispersive replication*.

Semiconservative replication yields one double-stranded DNA with ^{15}N DNA and one with ^{14}N DNA.

Dispersive replication would result in double-stranded DNA, with both strands having mixtures of ^{15}N and ^{14}N DNA, which would have appeared as DNA of an *intermediate density*.

22. C is correct.

DNA microarray (or *DNA chip*) collects microscopic DNA spots attached to a solid surface. DNA microarrays measure the expression levels of many genes or genotype multiple regions of a genome.

Each DNA spot contains picomoles (10^{-12} moles) of a specific DNA sequence.

Short sections of a gene (or other DNA element) hybridize cDNA *probes*.

An array simultaneously uses tens of thousands of probes; microarrays evaluate many genetic tests in parallel.

23. B is correct.

Avery, MacLeod, and McCarty (1944) demonstrated that DNA was the *transforming principle* for nonvirulent strains of pneumococcus.

Enzymes that destroyed nucleic acids destroyed the transforming activity, strengthening their hypothesis.

24. A is correct.

Codon-anticodon hybridization (i.e., bonding interaction) occurs between mRNA (*codon*) and tRNA (*anticodon*) during translation for protein synthesis.

25. B is correct.

Northern blot is a molecular biology technique to study gene expression by detecting RNA expression levels. Northern blotting uses electrophoresis to separate RNA samples by size. It involves the capillary transfer of RNA from the electrophoresis gel to the blotting membrane. It uses a hybridization probe via complementary hydrogen bonding to target expressed RNA fragments (i.e., expressed genes).

Eukaryotic mRNA is isolated using oligo (dT) cellulose chromatography to hybridize mRNA with a poly-A tail. The sample is resolved (i.e., separated) by gel electrophoresis.

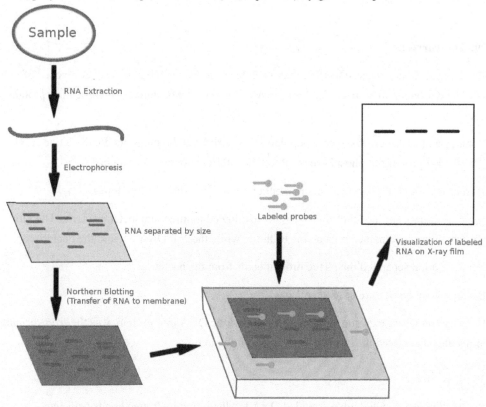

Northern blot uses RNA resolved by electrophoresis to evaluate gene expression using specific probes

Electrophoresis gels are fragile, and probes cannot enter the gel matrix. After resolution by electrophoresis, the size-separated RNA sample is transferred to a positively charged nylon (or nitrocellulose) membrane through capillary blotting. The negatively-charged mRNA adheres to the positive charge on the nylon.

In situ hybridization uses labeled probes of complementary DNA (cDNA) or RNA to localize a specific DNA or RNA sequence in a tissue section (*in situ*). Probes hybridize to the target sequence at an elevated temperature, and the excess probe is washed away.

---

26. E is correct.

Chromosomes replicate during the synthesis (S) phase of interphase.

27. E is correct.

DNA contains T, which is replaced with U in RNA.

28. B is correct.

Duplicated genes are closely related but diverged in sequence and function over evolutionary time.

29. D is correct.

Hershey and Chase showed in 1952 that when bacteriophages (i.e., viruses), composed of DNA and protein, infect bacteria, their DNA enters the host bacterial cell while their protein does not.

Hershey and Chase grew separate populations of viruses and incorporated radioactive sulfur (^{35}S to label protein) or phosphorus (^{32}P to label DNA) into the bacteriophages.

Two groups of viral progeny contained either ^{32}P or ^{35}S radioactive isotopes.

Separate aliquots of the labeled progeny were allowed to infect unlabeled bacteria. The viral ^{35}S protein coats remained outside the bacteria, while the ^{32}P DNA entered the bacteria.

Centrifugation separated the phage protein coats from the bacteria.

Bacteria were lysed to release the phages.

Hershey and Chase experiment demonstrated that the DNA, not protein, was the *transforming* molecule that entered the bacteria from a viral infection.

30. C is correct.

Replication forks open double-stranded DNA by disrupting hydrogen bonds between complementary nucleotide base pairs (e.g., A bonded to T and C bonded to G).

Gyrase cuts one strand of the DNA backbone and relaxes the positive supercoil that accumulates as helicase separates the two strands of DNA.

Ligase seals the backbone of DNA (i.e., joins Okazaki fragments) by forming phosphodiester bonds between deoxynucleotides in DNA.

31. A is correct.

Four atoms in the peptide bond are in the box.

Note that the oxygen on the carbonyl is oriented 180° from the H (antiperiplanar) on the nitrogen because the lone pair on the nitrogen participates in resonance, and the peptide bond is rigid (i.e., double bond like character).

32. D is correct.

DNA and ribozymes of RNA (discovered in 1982) are capable of self-replication.

Protein functions include:

     1) peptide hormones as chemical messengers transported within the blood,

     2) enzymes that catalyze chemical reactions by lowering the energy of activation,

     3) structural proteins for physical support within the cells, tissues, and organs,

     4) transport proteins as carriers of important materials, and

     5) immune system antibodies bind foreign particles (i.e., antigens).

33. B is correct.

Eukaryote RNA polymerase needs *transcription factors* (i.e., DNA binding proteins) to bind the promoter (on mRNA) and initiate basal-level transcription.

34. E is correct.

Percent of adenine cannot be determined because RNA is a single-stranded molecule.

Base-pairing rules for DNA (i.e., Chargaff's rule) are for double-stranded DNA but not single-stranded RNA.

35. A is correct.

I: AUG sequences are not only the initial start codon downstream of the initial *start codon* (AUG). If this sequence is not the start codon, this change could result in a stop codon (UAA).

II: *genetic code* is read 5′ to 3′ and AUG (encoding methionine) is a start codon.

A change in the start sequence in the mRNA (AUG to AAG) causes a failure in initiating translation.

III: changes in the first, second, or third amino acid may change U to A in the resultant amino acid.

The third position of the codon is the *wobble position* because the specified amino acid often does not change.

Nucleotide changes may not change the specified amino acid because the genetic code is redundant (i.e., most amino acids are encoded by more than one codon).

For example, AUU and AUA codons both encode isoleucine.

Genetic code is *degenerate*, whereby changing a nucleotide (often in the 3rd position) does not change the amino acid encoded by the triplet codon.

Each codon (three nucleotides) encodes for one amino acid, and there is no ambiguity in the genetic code.

36. B is correct.

Genetic code (mRNA into protein) has several amino acids specified by more than one codon, three stop codons, and each is 3 nucleotides (bases) long.

37. D is correct.

Polymerase I (Pol I) adds nucleotides at the RNA primer-template junction (i.e., the origin of replication) and is involved in excision repair with 3'-5' and 5'-3' exonuclease activity and processing of Okazaki fragments generated during lagging strand synthesis.

B: *primase* adds the first two RNA primers at the start of DNA replication because the DNA polymerase must bond to double-stranded molecules.

RNA primer is removed by DNA polymerase I after the newly synthesized DNA strand has been replicated via DNA polymerase III.

a: *template strand* of parental DNA

b: *leading strand* of newly synthesized DNA

c: *lagging strand* (Okazaki fragments) of newly   synthesized DNA

d: *replication fork* with helicase opening and unwinding the double-stranded DNA

e: *RNA primer* synthesized by primase

f: *direction* of DNA strand synthesis

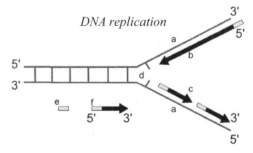

DNA replication

38. E is correct.

Okazaki fragments are associated with the lagging DNA strand and (like all DNA) are synthesized in a 5'→ 3' direction by DNA polymerase III.

A: DNA polymerase I removes the short sequence RNA primers deposited by primase needed for the anchoring of the polymerase III to DNA for the synthesis of DNA in a 5'→ 3' direction.

B: Okazaki fragments are used to replicate the lagging strand and are covalently linked by *DNA ligase* (not DNA polymerase I), forming a continuous DNA strand.

D: Okazaki fragments are not synthesized to fill in gaps after removing the RNA primer by DNA polymerase I.

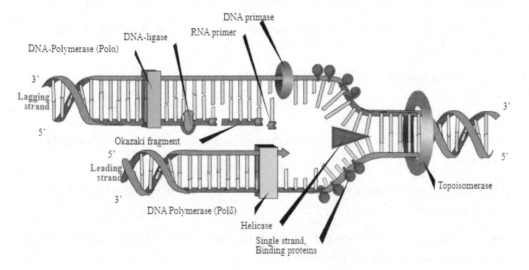

DNA semiconservative replication with associated proteins for leading and lagging strands.
DNA polymerase proceeds from 5' to 3' along parental strands.

39. C is correct.

Ribosomal RNAs (rRNA) form a large subunit and a small subunit.

During translation, mRNA is between the small and large subunits, and the ribosome catalyzes the formation of a peptide bond between the two amino acids held by the rRNA.

A single mRNA can be translated simultaneously by multiple ribosomes.

Ribosomes catalyze the formation of a *peptide bond* between two amino acids tethered by rRNA.

Ribosomes have three binding sites: A, P, and E.

Peptidyl transferase catalyzes this reaction.

187

A site binds an aminoacyl-tRNA (i.e., a tRNA bound to an amino acid).

Amino (NH_2) group of the aminoacyl-tRNA, with the new amino acid, attacks the ester linkage of peptidyl-tRNA (in the P site), the last amino acid of the growing chain, forming a new peptide bond.

tRNA holding the last amino acid moves to the E site, and the aminoacyl-tRNA is now the peptidyl-tRNA.

40. A is correct.

Protein synthesis does require energy.

B: rRNA is part of the ribosome and is necessary for proper binding of the ribosome to mRNA.

C: tRNA brings an amino acid to the ribosome, where it interacts with the mRNA of the proper sequence.

D: tRNA does have the amino acid bound to its 3' end.

41. B is correct.

Polymerase chain reaction (PCR) requires the sequence at the ends of the fragment to be amplified.

From the ends, primers use complementary base pairing to anneal the target fragment and permit amplification.

No knowledge of the region between the ends is required because the parent strands will be the template used by the DNA polymerase.

42. D is correct.

Shape of tRNA is determined primarily by *intramolecular base pairing*.

43. E is correct.

In prokaryotic cells, methylated guanine contributes to correcting mismatched pairs of bases.

44. A is correct.

Magnesium is a *divalent* mineral that DNA and RNA polymerases use as a cofactor (i.e., catalyst not consumed in the reaction) to stabilize interactions between polymerase and negative charge on the nucleic acid backbone.

45. C is correct.

Ribosome structure is created by the internal base-pairing of rRNA and ribosomal proteins.

46. A is correct.

Three types of RNA are *mRNA*, *tRNA*, and *rRNA*, which DNA encodes.

rRNA is synthesized in the nucleolus within the nucleus.

tRNA functions as a carrier of amino acid molecules.

Unlike mRNA, tRNA is a comparatively short ribonucleotide polymer of RNA subunits.

Although tRNA is single-stranded, there are double-stranded segments where the nucleotide chain loops back (i.e., hairpin turns) with hydrogen bonds between complementary base pairs; like DNA, two hydrogen bonds between A and U and three hydrogen bonds between C and G.

mRNA is the template for protein synthesis and has a poly-A tail, which functions as a *molecular clock* for mRNA degradation.

47. D is correct.

Phosphate group is the chemical group at the 5' end of a single polynucleotide strand.

48. E is correct.

Puromycin is an analog with a similar shape to tRNA.

Puromycin joins the ribosome, forms one peptide bond, and becomes covalently attached to the nascent protein.

However, since it lacks a carboxyl group, it cannot be linked to the next amino acid, and protein synthesis terminates prematurely.

Puromycin

A: *initiation* requires binding a single aminoacyl-tRNA (the initiator) to the ribosome and is unaffected.

B: *aminoacyl-tRNA* enters the large subunit of the ribosome at the A site during elongation.

D: *puromycin* lacks a carboxyl group and can only form one bond, so peptide synthesis stops prematurely.

49. C is correct.

In *E. coli* cells, DNA polymerase I degrades the RNA primer portion of Okazaki fragments.

50. D is correct.

DNA polymerase I proofreading increases replication fidelity by monitoring for mismatched pairs originating from the high processivity of polymerase III that rapidly replicates DNA.

Bacteria have a much lower DNA replication rate of about 1 in 1,000, increasing the mutation rate of bacteria.

51. C is correct.

DNA is a nucleotide polymer of the deoxyribose sugar, a phosphate group, and a nitrogenous base (e.g., A, C, G, T). Phosphodiester bonds join the nucleotides in DNA's backbone.

52. A is correct.

In *E. coli* cells, DNA polymerase III synthesizes most of the Okazaki fragments.

53. E is correct.

All the molecules, except cysteine, are nitrogenous bases – the component molecules of DNA and RNA (e.g., mRNA, rRNA & tRNA).

Nitrogenous bases guanine (G) and adenine (A) are purines, while cytosine (C) and thymine (T is in DNA) or uracil (U is in RNA) are pyrimidines.

Cysteine is an amino acid (not a nitrogenous base), and amino acids are the monomers for proteins.

54. A is correct.

Restriction enzyme (*restriction endonuclease*) cut DNA at specific nucleotide sequences (i.e., restriction sites).

Restriction enzymes are a defense mechanism against invading viruses in bacteria and archaea.

Prokaryotes have restriction enzymes that selectively cleave foreign DNA.

Host DNA is protected by a modification enzyme (i.e., methylase) that alters the prokaryotic DNA and prevents cleavage by the endogenous restriction enzyme.

55. C is correct.

RNA polymerase is an enzyme that produces primary transcript RNA in transcription.

Molecule C has a phosphodiester bond from the 3' of the base to the 5' downstream base and a triphosphate at the 5' end of the molecule.

A: represents DNA because of the absence of hydroxyl at the 2' position of the sugar.

B: contains a monophosphate at the 5' position.

D: shows a phosphodiester bond at the 2' position (not the 3').

E: shows a phosphodiester bond between two 5' ends.

First step, the two strands of the DNA double helix are physically separated at a high temperature in DNA melting.

Second step, the temperature is lowered, and two DNA strands become templates for DNA polymerase to selectively amplify the target DNA.

Third step, reaction mechanism uses RNA polymerase to synthesize a complementary strand to the template.

Selectivity of PCR results from using *primers complementary* to the DNA region targeted for amplification under specific *thermal cycling conditions*.

The process continues for 30 to 40 cycles, doubling the amount of DNA each cycle.

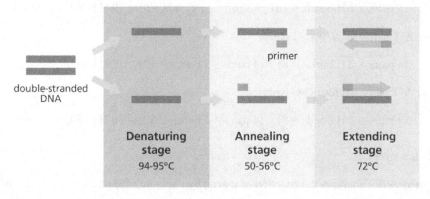

PCR amplification uses three steps for denaturing, annealing, and replicating DNA

57. A is correct.

DNA is double-stranded with A, C, G and T, while RNA is single-stranded with U replacing the T of DNA.

DNA uses the sugar of deoxyribose (i.e., the absence of ~OH group at the 2' in RNA), while RNA uses ribose (i.e., the presence of ~OH group at the 2').

58. B is correct.

Ligase is an enzyme used by the cell during DNA replication (and in other biochemical processes) that catalyzes the joining of two large molecules (e.g., DNA nucleotides) by forming a new chemical bond.

Newly formed bond is *via* a condensation reaction (joining) and usually involves dehydration with the loss of H_2O when the molecules (e.g., DNA, amino acids) are linked.

59. E is correct.

In DNA, thymine (T) base pairs with adenine (A) with two hydrogen bonds, while cytosine (C) base pairs with guanine (G) with three hydrogen bonds.

More energy is required to break three hydrogen bonds than two hydrogen bonds. A DNA sequence with increased C-G pairs has a higher melting point and requires more energy to denature (i.e., separate).

When bonded to its complementary strand, the DNA strand with GCCAGTCG has two T-A and six C-G pairs:

$$(2 \text{ pairs} \times 2 \text{ H bonds} = 4) + (6 \text{ pairs} \times 3 \text{ bonds} = 18) = 22 \text{ H bonds}$$

Thus, this DNA strand has the most hydrogen bonds and the highest melting point.

A: five T-A pairs and three C-G pairs:

$$(5 \text{ pairs} \times 2 \text{ H bonds} = 10) + (3 \text{ pairs} \times 3 \text{ bonds} = 9) = 19 \text{ H bonds}$$

C: four A-T pairs and four C-G pairs:

$$(4 \text{ pairs} \times 2 \text{ H bonds} = 8) + (4 \text{ pairs} \times 3 \text{ bonds} = 12) = 20 \text{ H bonds}$$

D: four A-T pairs and four C-G pairs:

$$(4 \text{ pairs} \times 2 \text{ H bonds} = 8) + (4 \text{ pairs} \times 3 \text{ bonds} = 12) = 20 \text{ H bonds}$$

60. C is correct.

Reverse genetics analyzes the function of a gene by observing the phenotypic effects of specific gene sequences obtained by DNA sequencing.

Reverse genetics seeks to find *which phenotypes* arise due to genetic sequences.

It proceeds in the opposite direction of classical genetics, which investigates the genetic basis of a phenotype.

61. D is correct.

Protein synthesis requires biochemical energy from ATP or GTP.

Two high-energy phosphate bonds (from ATP) provide the energy required to form one aminoacyl-tRNA involving the attachment of each amino acid to its tRNA.

> *Initiation complex* formation requires energy from one GTP.

> *Initiation* requires one high-energy phosphate bond (ATP) is required.

> *Elongation* with the delivery of each new tRNA to the A site requires one GTP.

> *Translocation* of the peptidyl-tRNA requires one GTP.

> *Termination* does not require the hydrolysis of a high-energy phosphate bond (e.g., ATP, GTP).

For each amino acid added to the polypeptide chain, two high-energy phosphate bonds are used for "charging" the tRNA with the correct amino acid (2 GTP × 50 amino acids = 100).

For chain formation, one high-energy phosphate bond is required to carry the amino acid to the ribosome and another to translocate the ribosome (2 GTP × 49 peptide bonds = 98).

> Total: 1 + 100 + 98 = 199

62. E is correct.

mRNA in *E. coli* cells is composed primarily of phosphodiester linkages between ribonucleotides.

63. B is correct.

DNA repair is a collection of processes by which a cell identifies and corrects damage to the DNA molecules encoding its genome.

Before replication of DNA, the cell methylates the parental strand for reference during any potential errors introduced during replication.

Normal metabolic activities and environmental factors such as UV light and radiation can cause DNA damage, resulting in many individual lesions per cell per day.

Many lesions cause structural damage to the DNA molecule and can alter the cell's ability to transcribe genes for the survival of its daughter cells after mitosis.

DNA repair process is constantly active as it responds to damage in the DNA structure, and methylation references the original strand when mismatches are detected during replication.

64. A is correct.

Methionine is the *start codon* of mRNA and is the first amino acid in eukaryotic proteins.

Mature protein may excise a portion of the original polypeptide, so methionine is not always the first amino acid in the mature protein after modification in the Golgi.

65. D is correct.

DNA in *E. coli* is composed of four bases (A, T, C, G), phosphodiester linkages connecting deoxyribonucleotide molecules;

two strands base pair in an anti-parallel orientation, and phosphodiester linkages utilizing the 3'-OH.

66. B is correct.

3'–CAGUCGUACUUU–5' anticodon of the tRNA (known from question stem)

5'–GUCAGCAUGAAA–3' codon of the mRNA

3'–CAGTCGTACTTT–5' DNA

There is a polarity when nucleic acids base pair, whereby the 3' end of the tRNA anticodon corresponds to the 5' end of the mRNA codon. C pairs with G, and U pairs with A (base pairing is U to A in RNA).

mRNA sequence is 5'–GUCAGCAUGAAA–3'.

3' end of the RNA hybridizes with the 5' end of DNA.

For complementary DNA, A pairs with T (not U in RNA), and the *polarity* of the strands is *antiparallel.*

An approach: since the 3' end of tRNA and the 3' end of DNA hybridize to the 5' of mRNA, the DNA sequence is the same orientation and similar to tRNA (i.e., replace T in DNA with U in tRNA).

By convention, nucleic acids are written with the 5' end on the left (top left in a double-stranded molecule) and read in the 5' to 3' direction.

67. A is correct.

Promoter is a region of 100–1000 base pairs long on the DNA that initiates transcription of a particular gene.

Promoters are near the genes they transcribe, on the same strand, and upstream on the DNA (towards the 3' region of the antisense strand – template and non-coding strand).

Promoters contain specific DNA sequences and response elements that provide a secure initial binding site for RNA polymerase and transcription factors proteins.

Transcription factors have specific activator (or repressor) sequences of nucleotides that attach to specific promoters and regulate gene expressions.

In bacteria, the promoter is recognized by RNA polymerase and an associated sigma factor (i.e., a protein needed only for initiation of RNA synthesis), which are often brought to the promoter DNA by an activator protein's binding to its own nearby DNA binding site.

In eukaryotes, the process is complicated, with many factors needed to bind RNA polymerase II to a promoter.

68. A is correct.

Isoleucine-glycine is composed of two amino acids and therefore is a dipeptide.

69. E is correct.

Correct order of events in delivering a protein to its cellular destination:

signal sequence binds to a docking protein → membrane channel forms → chaperonins unfold

70. D is correct.

RNA polymerase synthesizes the new strand in the anti-parallel orientation with new nucleotides adding to the growing chain in the 5' to 3' direction.

71. B is correct.

Adenosine (A) bonds with thymine (T) by two hydrogen bonds.

Guanine (G) bonds with cytosine (C) by three hydrogen bonds.

72. B is correct.

Lagging strand is composed of Okazaki fragments.

Nucleotides (e.g., DNA and RNA) extend from the 3'-OH group.

Leading (i.e., continuous) *and* lagging (i.e., discontinuous) strands use the 3'-OH ends as a *nucleophile* during condensation (i.e., via dehydration) reaction for chain elongation.

A: 3' end of the *template strand*.

C: 5' end of a *lagging strand*.

D: 5' end of the *template strand*

73. C is correct.

Ribosomal subunits, radio-labeled with *heavy* carbon and *heavy* nitrogen, were placed in a test tube during bacterial protein synthesis.

Small and large ribosomal subunits assemble to form a complete ribosome during translation.

After translation ceases, the complete ribosome dissociates into individual small and large subunits.

Since the sample used in centrifugation was taken after translation, the individual ribosomal subunits (not the assembled ribosomes) were present.

Centrifugation separates cellular components based on density, and since the subunits are varied sizes, two different bands are expected in the centrifuge tube.

Understanding the size of the two ribosomal subunits in bacteria is required; bacteria have two subunits of 30S and 50S, which assemble to form a 70S complex, and eukaryotes have 40S and 60s ribosomes, which assemble to form an 80S complex.

74. E is correct.

Translation is the protein production process whereby one amino acid adds to the end of a protein.

A ribosome performs this mechanism.

Sequence of nucleotides in the template mRNA chain determines the sequence of amino acids in the generated amino acid chain.

Adding an amino acid occurs at the C-terminus of the peptide, and translation is amino-to-carboxyl directed.

75. D is correct.

Codon for histidine is 5'-CAU-3'. The anticodon in tRNA that brings histidine to the ribosome is 5'-AUG-3'.

76. B is correct.

The existing polypeptide chain is transferred to the P site during translation elongation as the ribosome moves in the 3' direction.

77. A is correct.

In polymerase chain reactions (PCR amplification), a primer hybridizes to the end of a DNA fragment.

A primer is the initiation site for DNA polymerase to bind and replicate the entire strand.

DNA replicates $5' \rightarrow 3'$.

The primer must be the complement of the $3'$ end because DNA polymerase reads the template strand $3' \rightarrow 5'$.

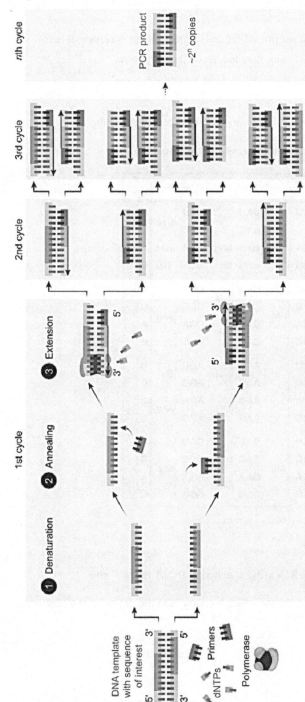

Polymerase chain with exponential product amplification during each cycle. First step heats the DNA to separate the two strands of the double helix. Step 2 cools the sample to allow annealing by complementary primers. Step 3 is chain elongation for the synthesis of DNA by RNA polymerase extending from the primers.

78. C is correct.

Genetic code is *not* ambiguous (i.e., each codon specifies one amino acid).

79. C is correct.

R-groups (i.e., amino acid side chains) portion of the polypeptide chain is responsible for establishing and maintaining the force to stabilize the secondary structure.

80. B is correct.

A ribosome made a tripeptide, MET-ARG-SER, attached to tRNA in the P site.

From the genetic code, the CGU codon is in the E site of the ribosome.

		Second base				
		U	**C**	**A**	**G**	
	U	UUU ⎤ Phe UUC ⎦ UUA ⎤ Leu UUG ⎦	UCU ⎤ UCC ⎥ Ser UCA ⎥ UCG ⎦	UAU ⎤ Tyr UAC ⎦ UAA Stop UAG Stop	UGU ⎤ Cys UGC ⎦ UGA Stop UGG Trp	U C A G
First base (5' end)	**C**	CUU ⎤ CUC ⎥ Leu CUA ⎥ CUG ⎦	CCU ⎤ CCC ⎥ Pro CCA ⎥ CCG ⎦	CAU ⎤ His CAC ⎦ CAA ⎤ Gln CAG ⎦	CGU ⎤ CGC ⎥ Arg CGA ⎥ CGG ⎦	U C A G	Third base (3' end)
	A	AUU ⎤ AUC ⎥ Ile AUA ⎦ AUG Met start	ACU ⎤ ACC ⎥ Thr ACA ⎥ ACG ⎦	AAU ⎤ Asn AAC ⎦ AAA ⎤ Lys AAG ⎦	AGU ⎤ Ser AGC ⎦ AGA ⎤ Arg AGG ⎦	U C A G
	G	GUU ⎤ GUC ⎥ Val GUA ⎥ GUG ⎦	GCU ⎤ GCC ⎥ Ala GCA ⎥ GCG ⎦	GAU ⎤ Asp GAC ⎦ GAA ⎤ Glu GAG ⎦	GGU ⎤ GGC ⎥ Gly GGA ⎥ GGG ⎦	U C A G

81. E is correct.

A ribosome made a tripeptide, MET-ARG-SER, attached to tRNA in the P site.

Using the genetic code, it cannot be determined which codon is in the A site of the ribosome.

82. E is correct.

Three *pyrimidines* are *cytosine* and *thymine* (*uracil* replaces thymine in RNA).

The word pyrimidine contains "**y**" as do the nucleotides, pyrimidines.

Pyrimidines (longer word than purine) are *one-ring structures*, while purines (shorter word) are adenine and guanine, larger structures with *two rings*.

83. D is correct.

Plasmid is a small DNA molecule separate from chromosomal DNA within a cell and replicates independently.

Commonly small, circular, double-stranded DNA molecules in bacteria, plasmids are sometimes in archaea and eukaryotic organisms.

In nature, plasmids carry genes that may benefit the organism's survival (e.g., antibiotic resistance in bacteria) and can be transmitted among bacteria, even of another species.

Artificial plasmids are commonly used as vectors in molecular cloning to drive the replication of recombinant DNA sequences within host organisms.

84. A is correct.

Plasmids are small circular double-stranded DNA in bacteria carrying *extrachromosomal genetic information*.

Plasmids (with an origin of replication) are replicated by bacterial proteins and inherited by progeny.

Proteins encoded by genes on plasmids often provide resistance to antibiotics by degrading the antibiotic.

Through recombinant DNA technology, plasmids are engineered to carry other genes *not typically in bacteria*.

Plasmids are introduced by *transforming* bacterial cells (i.e., through the cell wall and plasma membrane.

After transformation (i.e., uptake of DNA), exposure to the specific antibiotic (e.g., penicillin) allows the selection of bacteria transformed with the plasmid by clone selection (i.e., antibody-resistant clones).

85. A is correct.

Gene therapy focuses on genetically modifying cells to produce a therapeutic effect (or the treatment of disease) by repairing or reconstructing defective genetic material.

Notes for active learning

Notes for active learning

Notes for active learning

Practice Questions: Genetics

1. Which characteristic makes an organism unsuitable for genetic studies?

  A. Large number of chromosomes

  B. Short generation time

  C. Ease of cultivation

  D. Ability to control crosses

  E. Availability of a variation for traits

2. People with the sex-linked genetic disease hemophilia suffer from excessive bleeding because their blood will not clot. Tom, Mary, and their four daughters do not exhibit symptoms of hemophilia. However, their son exhibits symptoms of hemophilia because:

  A. Tom is heterozygous

  B. Tom is homozygous

  C. Mary is heterozygous

  D. Mary is homozygous

  E. All the above are equally probable

3. Several eye colors are characteristic of *Drosophila melanogaster*. Red eyes are dominant over sepia or white eyes. What percent of offspring of a sepia-eyed fly will have sepia eyes if mated with a red-eyed fly that was a cross of red-eyed and sepia-eyed parents?

  A. 0%

  B. 25%

  C. 50%

  D. 75%

  E. 100%

4. Color blindness mutations in humans result from:

  A. fragile X syndrome

  B. chromosome nondisjunction

  C. reciprocal translocation

  D. dosage compensation

  E. unequal crossing-over

5. Which method was NOT used by Mendel to study the genetics of garden peas?

  A. Maintenance of true-breeding lines

  B. Cross-pollination

  C. Microscopy

  D. Production of hybrid plants

  E. Quantitative analysis of results

6. Crossing AAbbCc × AaBbCc where A, B and C are unlinked genes, what is the probability of obtaining offspring with the AaBbCc genotype?

A. 1/4

B. 1/16

C. 1/64

D. 1/32

E. 1/8

7. What is the probability of having a child affected by a disease with an autosomal recessive inheritance if the mother and father are carriers of the disease?

A. 0%

B. 25%

C. 50%

D. 75%

E. 66%

8. For the multi-step progression of cancer, the major mutational target(s) is/are:

A. telomerase

B. X-linked traits

C. tumor suppressor gene

D. trinucleotide repeats

E. transcription factors

9. Since the gene responsible for color blindness is on the X chromosome, what is the probability that a son of a colorblind man and a woman carrier will be colorblind?

A. 75%

B. 100%

C. 25%

D. 50%

E. 66%

10. If two strains of true-breeding plants with alleles for a specific character are crossed, their progeny are:

A. P generation

B. F_1 generation

C. F_2 generation

D. F_1 crosses

E. F_2 progeny

11. The Arabidopsis plant has five pairs of homologous chromosomes. Suppose an Arabidopsis is heterozygous for five mutations, and each mutation is on a different chromosome. How many genetically distinct gametes will this plant make after meiosis?

A. 5

B. 10

C. 32

D. 64

E. 25

12. An unknown inheritance pattern has the following characteristics:

- 25% probability of having a homozygous unaffected child

- 25% probability of having a homozygous affected child

- 50% probability of having a heterozygous child

Which Mendel's inheritance pattern best matches the above observations?

A. autosomal recessive

B. autosomal dominant

C. X-linked recessive

D. X-linked dominant

E. cannot be determined without more information

13. What is the frequency of heterozygotes within a population in Hardy-Weinberg equilibrium if the frequency of the dominant allele D is three times that of the recessive allele d?

A. 7.25%   **C.** 33%

B. 12.75%   **D.** 37.5%

                             E. 50%

14. A recessive allele may appear in a phenotype due to:

A. gain-of-function mutation   **C.** senescence

B. acquired dominance   **D.** processivity

                                          E. the loss of heterozygosity

15. Which observations would support the theory of maternal inheritance for the spunky phenotype?

A. Spunky female x wild-type male → progeny all spunky

B. Wild-type female x spunky male → progeny all spunky

C. Wild-type female x spunky male → progeny 1/2 spunky, 1/2 wild-type

D. Spunky female x wild-type male → progeny 1/2 spunky, 1/2 wild-type

E. Spunky female x wild-type male → progeny all wild-type

16. Mendel concluded that each pea has two units for each characteristic, and each gamete contains one unit. Mendel's "unit" is now referred to as:

A. genome

B. hnRNA

C. codon

D. transcription factor

E. gene

17. Which leads to a complete loss of gene function?

A. A missense mutation that causes the nonpolar methionine to be replaced with glycine

B. GC base pair being converted to an AT base pair in the promoter

C. A mutation in the third codon of the open reading frame

D. A base pair change that does not affect the amino acid sequence

E. All the above

18. All effects are possible after a mutation, EXCEPT:

A. abnormal lipid production

B. abnormal protein production

C. gain of enzyme function

D. loss of enzyme function

E. no change in protein production

19. Which cross must produce all green, smooth peas if green (G) is dominant over yellow (g) and smooth (S) is dominant over wrinkled (s)?

A. GgSs × GGSS

B. GgSS × ggSS

C. Ggss × GGSs

D. GgSs × GgSs

E. None of the above

20. Retinoblastoma is inherited as:

A. a multifactorial trait

B. X-linked recessive

C. Mendelian dominant

D. Mendelian recessive

E. an extranuclear trait

21. Tay-Sachs disease is a rare autosomal recessive genetic disorder. If a male heterozygous carrier and a female heterozygous carrier have a first child who is homozygous wild type, what is the probability that the second child develops Tay-Sachs?

A. 1/3

B. 1/2

C. 1/16

D. 1/8

E. 1/4

22. Mendel's crossing of spherical-seeded pea plants with wrinkled-seeded pea plants resulted in progeny that all had spherical seeds. This indicates that the wrinkled-seed trait is:

A. codominant

B. dominant

C. recessive

D. penetrance

E. codominant and recessive

23. The result of mitosis is the production of:

A. two (1N) cells identical to the parent cell

B. two (2N) cells identical to the parent cell

C. four (1N) cells identical to the parent cell

D. four (2N) cells identical to the parent cell

E. four (1N) unique cells that are genetically different from the parent cell

24. The degree of genetic linkage is often measured by the:

A. frequency of nonsense mutations

B. histone distribution

C. frequency of missense mutations

D. probability of crossing over

E. AT/GC ratio

25. Cancers associated with defects in mismatch repair are inherited via:

A. dominant inheritance

B. maternal inheritance

C. X-linked inheritance

D. epigenetic inheritance

E. recessive inheritance

26. Given that color blindness is a recessive trait inherited through a sex-linked gene on the X chromosome, what probability will a daughter born to a colorblind father and a mother carrier be a carrier?

A. 0%

B. 25%

C. 50%

D. 100%

E. 12.5%

27. What is the probability that a cross between a true-breeding pea plant with a dominant trait and a true-breeding pea plant with a recessive trait will result in all F_1 progeny having the dominant trait?

A. 50%

B. 25%

C. 0%

D. 100%

E. 12.5%

28. The tall allele is dominant to short. True-breeding tall plants were crossed with true-breeding short plants. The F_1 plants were self-crossed to produce F_2 progeny. What are the phenotypes of the F_1 and F_2 progeny?

    A. All F_1 and 1/4 of the F_2 are short

    B. All F_1 are short, and 1/4 of the F_2 are tall

    C. All F_1 and 3/4 of the F_2 are tall

    D. All F_1 are tall, and 3/4 of the F_2 plants are short

    E. All the above are equally probable

29. All DNA lesions result in a frameshift mutation, EXCEPT:

    A. 1 inserted base pair

    B. 2 substituted base pairs

    C. 4 inserted base pairs

    D. 2 deleted base pairs

    E. 5 deleted base pairs

30. If two species with the AaBbCc genotype reproduce, what is the probability that their progeny have the AABBCC genotype?

    A. 1/2

    B. 1/4

    C. 1/16

    D. 1/64

    E. 1/8

31. At the hypoxanthine-guanine phosphoribosyltransferase (HPRT) locus, an average amount of mRNA is present, but no protein is observed. This phenotype is caused by the following:

    A. frameshift mutation

    B. mutation in the gene-altering the restriction pattern but not affecting the protein; for instance, the mutated nucleotide is in the third codon position of the open reading frame

    C. point mutation leading to an amino acid substitution necessary for enzyme function

    D. gene deletion or mutation affecting the promoter

    E. nonsense mutation affecting message translation

32. Hemophilia is a recessive X-linked trait. Knowing that females with Turner's syndrome have a high incidence of hemophilia, it can be concluded that these females have:

    A. lost an X and gained a Y

    B. lost an X

    C. gained an X

    D. gained a Y

    E. none of the above

33. What is the pattern of inheritance for a rare recessive allele?

    A. Every affected person has an affected parent

    B. Unaffected parents can produce children who are affected

    C. Unaffected mothers have affected sons and daughters who are carriers

    D. Every affected person produces an affected offspring

    E. None of the above

34. True-breeding plants with large purple flowers were crossed with true-breeding plants with small white flowers. The F_1 progeny all had large purple flowers. The F_1 progeny were crossed to true-breeding plants with small white flowers. Among 1000 progeny:

Number of progeny	Flower size	Flower color
250	small	white
250	small	purple
250	large	white
250	large	purple

Most likely, the genes for flower size and color:

    A. are unlinked

    B. are sex-linked

    C. are linked and separated by no more than 25 centimorgans

    D. require determination of the cross of the F_2 progeny

    E. cannot be determined

35. If tall height and brown eye color are dominant, what is the probability for a heterozygous tall, heterozygous, brown-eyed mother and a homozygous tall, homozygous, blue-eyed father to have a tall child with blue eyes? Note: the genes for eye color and height are unlinked.

    A. 3/4   **C.** 1/4

    B. 1/8   **D.** 1/2

                                 E. None of the above

36. Recombination frequencies:

    A. are the same for *cis-* and *trans*-heterozygotes

    B. arise from completely random genetic exchanges

    C. decrease with distance

    D. are the same for all genes

    E. are the same for all chromosomes

37. How many different gametes can be produced from the genotype AaBbCc, assuming independent assortment?

    A. 4   **C.** 8

    B. 6   **D.** 16

                         E. 3

38. What is the pattern of inheritance for a rare dominant allele?

    A. Every affected person has an affected parent

    B. Unaffected parents can produce children who are affected

    C. Unaffected mothers have affected sons and daughters who are carriers

    D. Every affected person produces an affected offspring

    E. All the above

39. Individuals homozygous for an autosomal recessive mutation accumulate harmful amounts of lipids. Jane and her parents are not afflicted. However, Jane's sister accumulates lipids. What is the probability that Jane is heterozygous for the mutation?

    A. 1/4   **C.** 2/3

    B. 1/3   **D.** 1/2

                         E. 3/4

40. A genetic disease with early-onset and severe symptoms with every generation is an example of:

    A. codominance   **C.** heterozygous advantage

    B. penetrance   **D.** gain-of-function mutations

                             E. anticipation

41. For a trait with two alleles, if the recessive allele frequency is 0.6 in a population, what is the frequency of individuals expressing the dominant phenotype?

A. 0.48

B. 0.64

C. 0.16

D. 0.36

E. 0.12

42. The maximum recombination frequency between two genes is:

A. 100%

B. 80%

C. 50%

D. 10%

E. 1%

43. In mice, short hair is dominant over long hair. If a short-haired individual is crossed with a long-haired individual, and both long and short-haired offspring result, what can be concluded?

A. Short-haired individual is homozygous

B. Short-haired individual is heterozygous

C. Long-haired individual is homozygous

D. Long-haired individual is heterozygous

E. More information is required

44. The result of meiosis in males is the production of:

A. two (1N) cells genetically identical to the parent cell

B. two (2N) cells genetically identical to the parent cell

C. four (1N) cells genetically identical to the parent cell

D. four (1N) unique cells genetically different from the parent cell

E. four (2N) cells genetically identical to the parent cell

45. Which is a type of genetic mutation?

I.   insertion   II. frameshift   III. nonsense   IV. missense

A. I and II only

B. I, II and III only

C. II and IV only

D. I, II, III and IV

E. II, III and IV only

46. Two reciprocal crossing-over events appear in the progeny at an approximate ratio of:

   A. 4:1

   B. 3:1

   C. 2:1

   D. 2:3

   E. 1:1

47. In dogs, phenotype A (erect ears and barking while following a scent) is caused by dominant alleles; recessive alleles cause phenotype B (droopy ears and silent while following a scent). A dog that is homozygous dominant for both traits is mated with a dog that is homozygous recessive for both traits. If the two genes are unlinked, which is the expected F_1 phenotypic ratio?

   A. 9:3:3:1

   B. 1:1

   C. 16:0

   D. 1:2:1

   E. None of the above

48. Mutations:

   A. always cause severe mutant phenotypes

   B. never cause severe mutant phenotypes

   C. are not inherited by the progeny

   D. may cause premature termination of translation

   E. are none of the above

49. What is the probability of having a child affected by a disease with autosomal dominant inheritance if both the mother and father have one mutant gene for that disease?

   A. 0%

   B. 25%

   C. 50%

   D. 12.5%

   E. 75%

50. Given the recombinant frequencies below, what is the sequence of linked genes D, E, F and G?

GE: 23%	ED: 15%	EF: 8%
GD: 8%	GF: 15%	DF: 7%

   A. FGDE

   B. EFGD

   C. GFDE

   D. GDFE

   E. DEFG

Questions **51** through **57** are based on the following:

The pedigree illustrated by the schematic shows the inheritance of albinism, a homozygous recessive condition manifested in a lack of pigment. Specify the genotypes using *A* and *a* to indicate dominant and recessive alleles.

Note: solid figures are albino individuals.

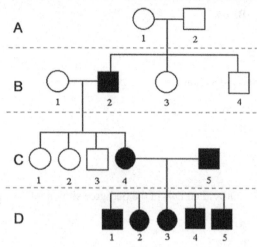

51. Individual A-1 in the pedigree shown is:

  A. *AA*
  B. *aa*
  C. *Aa*
  D. any of the above
  E. none of the above

52. Individual A-2 in the pedigree shown is:

  A. *AA*
  B. *aa*

  C. *Aa*
  D. any of the above
  E. none of the above

53. Individual B-1 in the pedigree shown is:

  A. *AA*
  B. *aa*

  C. *Aa*
  D. any of the above
  E. none of the above

54. Individual B-2 in the pedigree shown is:

  A. *AA*
  B. *aa*

  C. *Aa*
  D. any of the above
  E. none of the above

55. Individual C-3 in the pedigree shown is:

A. *AA*

B. *aa*

C. *Aa*

D. any of the above

E. none of the above

56. Individual C-4 in the pedigree shown is:

A. *AA*

B. *aa*

C. *Aa*

D. any of the above

E. none of the above

57. Individual D-4 in the pedigree shown is:

A. *AA*

B. *aa*

C. *Aa*

D. any of the above

E. none of the above

58. In cocker spaniels, black color (B) is dominant over red (b), and solid color (S) is dominant over spotted (s). If the genes are unlinked and the offspring of BBss and bbss individuals are mated, what fraction of their offspring will be black and spotted?

A. 1/16

B. 9/16

C. 1/9

D. 3/16

E. 3/4

59. Why do genes that cause disease often appear to skip generations in an X-linked recessive inheritance?

A. The disease is primarily transmitted through unaffected carrier females

B. Males with an affected gene are carriers but do not show the disease

C. X-linked diseases are only expressed in males

D. All X-linked diseases display incomplete penetrance

E. none of the above

60. The "calico" coat pattern of a female cat is a result of:

A. endoreduplication

B. unequal crossing-over

C. random X chromosome inactivation

D. Turner syndrome

E. trisomy of the X chromosome

61. Which statement is true for an autosomal dominant inheritance?

    I. A single allele of the mutant gene is needed to exhibit the phenotype

    II. Transmission to the son by the father is not observed

    III. Autosomal dominant traits do not skip generations

A. II only

B. I, II and III

C. I only

D. I and III only

E. II and III only

62. What chromosomal abnormality results in some XY individuals being phenotypically females?

A. fragile X syndrome

B. Barr body formation

C. dosage compensation

D. mosaicism

E. portion deleted of the Y chromosome with the testis-determining factor

63. Which event risks combining two recessive alleles, resulting in a genetic defect?

A. genetic mutation

B. transformation

C. inbreeding

D. crossing over

E. trisomy

64. To engineer polyploid plants in plant breeding, genetic engineers use drugs that:

A. insert new DNA into plants' genome

B. damage the DNA and cause mutations

C. rearrange the sequences of codons on the DNA strand

D. alter the number of chromosomes

E. shorten the length of DNA strands

65. To create mules, horses are bred with donkeys by:

A. crossing over

B. genetic engineering

C. hybridization

D. inbreeding

E. genetic mutation

66. When treated with penicillin, a bacterial culture transformed with recombinant plasmids that contain a gene for resistance to this antibiotic will:

A. undergo lysis

B. rapidly replicate DNA

C. die

D. survive

E. alternate generations

67. Which pairing represents two transgenic organisms?

A. Appletree hybrid and a polyploid cherry tree

B. Human growth hormone-producing bacteria and genetically modified soybeans

C. Appletree hybrid and human growth hormone-producing bacteria

D. Genetically modified soybeans and a polyploid cherry tree

E. Polyploid cherry tree and human growth hormone-producing bacteria

68. Which choice correctly describes the process of establishing parental relationships through DNA fingerprinting of specific genes?

A. Mitochondrial DNA links a daughter to the mother, while plasmid DNA links to the father

B. Mitochondrial DNA links a son to the mother, while the Y chromosome links to the father

C. X chromosome links a daughter to the mother, while the Y chromosome links to the father

D. X chromosome links a son to the mother, while mitochondrial DNA links to the father

E. Y chromosome links a son to the mother, while the X chromosome links a girl to the father

69. Which inheritance pattern is when an affected male has all affected daughters but no affected sons?

A. X-linked recessive

B. Y-linked

C. Autosomal dominant

D. Autosomal recessive

E. X-linked dominant

Notes or active learning

Notes or active learning

Detailed Explanations: Genetics

Answer Key

1: A	11: C	21: E	31: E	41: B	51: C	61: D
2: C	12: A	22: C	32: B	42: C	52: C	62: E
3: C	13: D	23: B	33: B	43: B	53: C	63: C
4: E	14: E	24: D	34: A	44: D	54: B	64: D
5: C	15: A	25: A	35: D	45: D	55: C	65: C
6: E	16: E	26: C	36: A	46: E	56: B	66: D
7: B	17: B	27: D	37: C	47: C	57: B	67: B
8: C	18: A	28: C	38: A	48: D	58: E	68: B
9: D	19: A	29: B	39: C	49: E	59: A	69: E
10: B	20: C	30: D	40: E	50: D	60: C	

1. A is correct.

Model organism for *genetic studies* (e.g., pea plants, Drosophila, zebrafish) has common features. The organism must be bred in *large numbers*, and *ease of cultivation* favors viable offspring that *transmit genetic information* between generations.

Genetic studies rely upon statistics that favor *large sample numbers*. Therefore, a short generation time (i.e., the span between birth and fecundity) is preferred.

There should be *discreet phenotypic differences* among alleles (alternative forms of the gene).

For example, among the seven traits Mendel (1822-1884) observed, he inventoried tall *vs.* short plants, round *vs.* smooth seeds, and green *vs.* yellow seeds.

Mendel controlled the crosses by manually transferring pollen from the anther of a mature pea plant of one variety to the stigma of a separate mature pea plant of the second variety.

Organisms should have a *well-characterized genome* (gene identity and function have been studied).

Increasing *numbers of chromosomes* increase the genes that can influence the observable phenotypic outcomes.

Fewer chromosomes facilitate statistical analysis and causation when the genome is manipulated.

2. C is correct.

Sex-linked genetic disease, hemophilia, causes excessive bleeding because the blood does not clot. Tom, Mary, and their four daughters do not exhibit symptoms of hemophilia.

However, their son exhibits symptoms of hemophilia because Mary is heterozygous.

3. C is correct.

Eye color is sex-linked in *Drosophila*.

Determine the phenotype of parents.

Red-eyed flies with red-eyed and sepia-eyed parents must be heterozygous because a sepia-eyed parent only contributes recessive sepia alleles.

When a heterozygous (Rr) red-eyed fly is crossed with a homozygous recessive (rr) sepia-eyed fly, ½ of the offspring are red-eyed (Rr) because of the dominant (red) allele from the heterozygous fly.

Punnett Square:

Red eyed parent

	R	r
r	Rr (red)	rr (sepia)
r	Rr (red)	rr (sepia)

Sepia eyed Parent (left column)

Since the question does not assign gender to the sepia and red-eyed parents, the Punnett squares for two combinations for sex-linked traits are:

Red eyed female (♀)

	R	r
r	Rr (red)	rr (sepia)
y	Ry (red)	ry (sepia)

Sepia eyed male (♂)

Red eyed male (♂)

	R	y
r	Rr (red)	ry (sepia)
r	Rr (red)	ry (sepia)

Sepia eyed female (♀)

4. E is correct.

Color blindness pertains to cone photoreceptors in retinas, as the cones can detect the color frequencies of light.

About 8 percent of males, but 0.5 percent of females, are colorblind, whether it is one color, a color combination, or another mutation.

Males are at a greater risk of inheriting an X-linked mutation because males have one X chromosome (XY) while females have two (XX).

Men lack a second X chromosome to compensate for the X chromosome that carries the gene mutation.

If a woman inherits a typical X chromosome in addition to the one that carries the mutation, she does not display the mutation.

5. C is correct.

Microscopy is the laboratory technique of magnifying objects that cannot be seen with the unaided eye.

Gregor Mendel (1822-1884) performed crossbreeding experiments with pea plants to study inheritance patterns and introduced the terms *dominant* and *recessive* for phenotypic traits (or *alleles*).

6. E is correct.

AAbbCc produces 2 gametes:

AbC and Abc = 1/2

AaBbCc produces 8 gametes:

ABC, ABc, AbC, Abc, aBC, aBc, abC, abc = 2/8 possible = 1/4

From probability: 1/2 × 1/4 = 1/8

	ABC	ABc	AbC	Abc	aBC	aBc	abC	abc
AbC	X	X	X	X	X	**Yes**	X	X
Abc	X	X	X	X	**Yes**	X	X	X

7. B is correct.

Afflicted children are aa = 1 of 4 possibilities = ¼ or 25%.

	A	a
A	AA	Aa
a	Aa	**aa**

8. C is correct.

Tumor suppressor genes protect a cell from aberrant cell cycles.

When this gene's function is lost or reduced due to mutation, the cell can progress to cancer (usually combined with other genetic mutations).

Loss of tumor suppressor genes may be more critical than proto-oncogene/oncogene activation to form many kinds of human cancer cells.

Both alleles of the tumor suppressor gene encoding a particular protein must be affected before an effect is manifested.

If one allele is damaged, the second can produce the correct protein.

9. D is correct.

Color blindness is a *sex-linked trait* because the gene is on the X chromosome.

Mother is a carrier (not afflicted with condition) and is heterozygous for the recessive allele (color blindness).

Father has the allele on his X chromosome (Y chromosome lacks the gene).

Genotype and *phenotype* of an XY son depend entirely on the mother (afflicted vs. carrier) since the afflicted father transmits the gene on his X.

Mother is heterozygous; a son has a 50% probability of receiving the color-blindness allele from his mother.

10. B is correct.

If two strains of true-breeding plants with different alleles are crossed, their progeny is the F_1 generation.

11. C is correct.

$$AaBbCcDdEe \times AaBbCcDdEe$$

From probability:

$$\tfrac{1}{2} \times \tfrac{1}{2} \times \tfrac{1}{2} \times \tfrac{1}{2} \times \tfrac{1}{2} = 1/32$$

12. A is correct.

Autosomal recessive inheritance is the product of mating two carriers (i.e., heterozygous parents).

In mating two heterozygotes for an autosomal recessive gene, there is a:

25% (1/4) probability of a homozygous *unaffected* child

25% (1/4) probability of a homozygous *affected* child

50% (1/2) probability of a heterozygous (*carrier*) child

75% of children are phenotypically normal (25% AA and 50% Aa).

Of all children, 50% are phenotypically normal but carry the mutant gene (Aa).

13. D is correct.

If the dominant allele frequency is three times that of the recessive allele,

$$p = 3q$$

Hardy-Weinberg equilibrium:

$$p + q = 1$$

so

$$3q + q = 1$$

Solving for q

$$4q = 1$$

$$q = 0.25$$

$$p = 0.75$$

Allele frequency:

$$p^2 + 2pq + q^2 = 1$$

Heterozygote allele = 2pq

Substituting for p and q,

$$2(0.75) \cdot (0.25) = 0.375 \text{ or } 37.5\%$$

14. E is correct.

Loss of heterozygosity is a chromosomal event resulting from losing the gene and surrounding region.

Diploid cells (e.g., human somatic cells) contain *two copies* of the genome, one from each parent.

Each copy contains approximately 3 billion bases, and for most positions in the genome, the base is consistent between individuals. However, a small percentage may contain different bases.

These positions are *single nucleotide polymorphisms* (or SNP). The region is heterozygous when the genomic copies from each parent have different bases for these regions.

Most chromosomes within somatic cells are paired, allowing SNP locations to be potentially heterozygous.

One parental copy of a region can be lost, resulting in the region with just one copy.

If the copy lost contained the dominant allele, the remaining recessive allele would appear in a phenotype.

15. A is correct.

Maternal inheritance involves all progeny exhibiting the phenotype of the *female* parent.

B: not maternal inheritance because the progeny exhibits the phenotype of the *male* parent.

C and D: Mendelian 1:1 segregation and not maternal inheritance.

Maternal inheritance is uniparental when all progeny have the genotype and phenotype of the female parent.

16. E is correct.

Gene is a fundamental physical, functional unit of heredity transferred from a parent to offspring and determines some offspring characteristics.

Genes are DNA sequences encoding proteins.

Alleles are forms of the same gene with slight differences in their sequence of DNA bases.

Genome is the *complete set of genetic information* for an organism.

Genome has the genetic information needed for an organism and allows it to develop, grow and reproduce.

17. B is correct.

GC base pairs converted to AT base pairs in the promoter will likely lose gene function completely.

18. A is correct.

Mutations affect proteins but not lipids or carbohydrates.

In proteins, the effects on the protein are no change (i.e., silent mutation), abnormal protein production, loss of protein (enzyme) function, or gain of protein (enzyme) function.

Loss of function of a gene product may result from mutations encoding a regulatory element or the loss of critical amino acid sequences.

Gain-of-function mutations are changes in the amino acids resulting in enhancement of the protein function.

There may be an increase in the level of protein expression (affecting the operator region of the gene) or an increase in each protein molecule's ability to perform its function (change in the shape of the protein).

19. A is correct.

The desired phenotype is green smooth peas, and green and smooth are dominant phenotypes.

Therefore, the genotypes selected for the cross must avoid the two recessive alleles (g and s).

For GgSs × GGSS, one parent (GGSS) is a double dominant, and therefore all offspring have the dominant phenotype (G and S) regardless of the other parent's genotype.

B: Gg × gg yields 1/2 yellow (g) phenotype offspring

C: ss × Ss yields 1/2 wrinkled (s) phenotype offspring

D: Gg × Gg yields 1/4 yellow (g) phenotype offspring

20. C is correct.

Retinoblastoma (Rb) is a rapidly developing cancer in immature cells of the retina, the light-detecting tissue of the eye. It is a common malignant tumor of the eyes in children. A single allele is inherited (i.e., dominant) for the phenotype.

21. E is correct.

Phenotype of the first child does not influence the probability of the second child.

For example, the probability of getting a tail on the first toss of a coin does not influence the probability of getting a head on the second toss.

Punnett square determines possible gametes and their combinations.

If ½ of the woman's gametes carry the trait and ½ of the father's gametes carry the trait, the probability of a child receiving the allele from each parent is ½ × ½ = ¼.

22. C is correct.

In Mendel's experiment, the cross of spherical-seeded and wrinkled-seeded pea plants inherited alleles (or *gene variants*) from each parent.

However, only spherical-seeded plants resulted from the cross.

Wrinkled-seed gene is a recessive allele compared to the spherical-seed gene (i.e., the dominant gene).

Dominant allele is a genetic variant expressed more strongly than other variants (or alleles) of the gene (i.e., recessive) for many reasons.

23. B is correct.

Notation 2N indicates that a given cell line is diploid, two homologous versions of each chromosome.

Human somatic cells are diploid with 23 different chromosome pairs (N = 23) for 46 chromosomes (2N = 46).

Gamete cells (eggs and sperm) are haploid (i.e., 1N).

Mitosis is the mode of cell division used by somatic cells, resulting in two diploid daughter cells genetically identical to the diploid parent cell.

24. D is correct.

Degree of genetic linkage measures the physical distance of two genes on the same chromosome.

Probability of crossover and corresponding exchange between gene loci (location on the chromosome) is generally proportional to the distance between the loci.

Genes far apart on a chromosome are more likely to be separated during crossover than genes physically close.

Thus, *frequency of genetic recombination* between two genes is *related to their distance*.

Recombination frequencies are used to construct genetic maps.

One map unit (Morgan units) is defined as a 1 percent recombinant frequency.

Recombination frequencies are roughly *additive* and are a good approximation for small percentages.

Largest percentage of recombinants cannot exceed 50%, resulting when the two genes are at the opposite ends of the same chromosome.

Crossover events result in an exchange of genes.

However, an odd number of crossover events (a 50% probability between an even and an odd number of crossover events) results in a recombinant product.

25. A is correct.

Epigenetic inheritance results from changes in gene activity, *not* caused by changes in the DNA sequence.

It studies stable, long-term alterations in the transcriptional potential that are not necessarily heritable.

Unlike simple genetics based on changes to the DNA sequence (genotype), the changes in gene expression or cellular phenotype of epigenetics have other causes.

For example, *cellular differentiation* is an epigenetic change in eukaryotes cells.

During *morphogenesis*, totipotent (i.e., all potent) stem cells become pluripotent (i.e., highly potent, but with limited determinate potential) cells of the embryo, which become fully differentiated cells.

Gene expression is when a single fertilized egg cell (zygote) divides, and the resulting daughter cells change into different cell types (e.g., neurons, muscle cells, epithelium, endothelium of blood vessels) by activating some genes while inhibiting the expression of others.

26. C is correct.

Female children receive one X from their mother and one X from their father.

X from the father must carry the color-blindness allele because the father is colorblind.

X from the mother has a wild-type and a color blindness allele because she is heterozygous recessive.

50% of female children are homozygous colorblind, and 50% are heterozygous carriers.

27. D is correct.

True breeding means that the organism is homozygous (e.g., AA or aa) for the trait.

All progeny are heterozygous Aa (below) and exhibit the dominant phenotype.

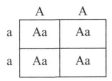

28. C is correct.

	A	A
a	Aa	Aa
a	Aa	Aa

	A	a
A	AA	Aa
a	Aa	aa

F_1: all tall F_2: ¾ are tall, and ¼ is short

29. B is correct.

Frameshift mutation is when 1 or 2 base pairs are added or deleted. A 3 base pair addition or deletion causes an *in-frame* mutation because 3 nucleotides encode each codon.

Frameshift mutation (i.e., addition/deletion of other than multiples of 3 nucleotides) causes the ribosome to read all downstream codons in the wrong frame. They usually result in truncated (i.e., *nonsense* mutation) or non-functional proteins (i.e., *missense* mutation).

An altered base pair (i.e., *point* mutation) is not a frameshift mutation because it substitutes (not adds or deletes) and does not cause the ribosome to read codons out of frame.

Point mutations can result in nonsense (i.e., premature stop codon) or missense (i.e., improperly folded protein) mutations.

Base pair additions/deletions (other than in multiples of 3) cause frameshift mutations.

30. D is correct.

Mendel's *law of independent assortment* states that the probability of a cross resulting in a genotype equals the *product* of individual probabilities.

Crosses by two heterozygous individuals for the three genes (A, B, and C) produce homozygous dominant offspring for each trait.

Each parent is heterozygous for A, genotype = Aa.

Ratio of offspring equals 1/4 AA, 1/2 Aa, and 1/4 aa; a typical 1:2:1 ratio for heterozygous crosses.

Parents are heterozygous for genes B and C, the probability of offspring being BB is 1/4, and CC is 1/4.

Probability that offspring are genotype AABBCC = *product of individual probabilities*:

$$1/4 \times 1/4 \times 1/4 = 1/64$$

31. E is correct.

Nonsense mutation is a DNA point mutation resulting in a premature stop codon in the transcribed mRNA and a truncated (i.e., incomplete) protein, usually nonfunctional.

Missense mutation is a point mutation where a nucleotide is changed and substitutes for a different amino acid.

Genetic disorders of sickle cell anemia, thalassemia and Duchenne muscular dystrophy arise from *nonsense mutations*.

32. B is correct.

Recessive trait is expressed when present in both copies (i.e., alleles) or is the single copy of the gene.

Human Y chromosome confers maleness.

Recessive (single copy) alleles on the X are expressed (e.g., hemophilia).

Recessive X-linked allele is expressed in unaffected females with two (homozygous) alleles.

33. B is correct.

Mendelian *Laws of inheritance* explain patterns of disease transmission.

Inheritance patterns of single-gene diseases are *Mendelian* after Augustinian friar Gregor Mendel (1822-1884), who first reported different gene segregation patterns for specific garden peas traits.

Mendel calculated *probabilities* of inheritance for traits in the next generations.

Because of mutations or polymorphisms, most genes have more versions (i.e., alleles).

Individuals carry normal, mutant, or rare alleles, depending on mutation/polymorphism and allele frequency within a population.

Single-gene diseases are usually inherited depending on gene location and whether one or two regular copies of the gene are needed for the disease to manifest (i.e., affected individuals).

Expression of a mutated allele is *dominant, co-dominant*, or *recessive*.

Five basic *patterns of inheritance for single-gene diseases*:

Autosomal dominant:

each affected person has an affected parent

manifests in each generation

Autosomal recessive:

parents of an affected person are carriers (i.e., unaffected)

typically, NOT seen in each generation

X-linked dominant:

females affected more frequently

can affect males and females in the same generation

X-linked recessive:

males affected more frequently

often affects males in each generation

Mitochondrial:

males and females can be affected but passed by females

can appear in each generation

An accurate family history is essential to determine inheritance pattern when a family is affected by a disease.

34. A is correct.

Two traits are *unlinked* when inherited on separate chromosomes or because the genes are apart greater than 50 centimorgans.

At large distances, double-crossing over occurs, and the genes appear unlinked.

35. D is correct.

Let T = tall and t = short; B = brown eyes and b = blue eyes.

Father is *homozygous tall* and *blue-eyed*; his genotype is TTbb.

Mother is *heterozygous tall* and *heterozygous brown-eyed*; her genotype is TtBb.

Determine the probability that parents produce a tall child with blue eyes (T_bb).

The genes for height and eye color are unlinked.

Father (TTbb) contributes T and b alleles, so his gametes have T and b alleles.

Mother (TtBb) contributes T or t and B or b, so her gametes are (in equal amounts): TB, tB, Tb, or tb.

Genotypes of the offspring:

> TTBb, TTbb, TtBb, Ttbb

Half the offspring are tall and brown-eyed (T_B_), and half are tall and blue-eyed (T_bb).

Therefore, the probability of a tall child with blue eyes is ½.

A faster method is calculating phenotype ratios for height and eye color separately and then combining them.

> Mating TT × Tt = 100% tall
>
> Mating Bb × Bb = ½ blue and ½ brown
>
> Multiplying 1 tall × ½ blue = ½ tall blue

36. A is correct.

Recombination is the exchange of genetic information between homologous chromosomes and occurs during prophase I of meiosis.

Crossing over between non-sister homologs in *meiosis* results in a new combination of alleles, for example:

> AB / ab can yield Ab / aB

Recombination occurs in eukaryotes during *mitosis* but between *sister chromatids* which are copies (replicated during the S phase) and therefore do *not* lead to novel genotypes.

Recombination is a *DNA repair mechanism* between homologous chromosomes.

Research supports that recombination is not a random event.

231

Recombination hotspots include chromosome regions with *high GC content* and particular architecture (e.g., genome size, haploid chromosome number, chromosome size, and chromosome rearrangements).

Enzymes catalyze recombination (e.g., rec A, rec B, rec C, and rec D) by initiating and *facilitating strand invasion* and *strand transfer* during recombination.

High recombination frequency means the genes are *farther apart*.

Each percent frequency of recombination equals one map unit between the genes. So, 2.5% recombination frequency equals genes 2.5 map units apart.

Largest recombination frequency is 50%, as if the genes were on different chromosomes (consistent with Mendel's Law of Independent Assortment).

Recombination frequency would be the same for *cis-* and *trans*-heterozygotes because the distance is the same between the genes regardless of whether they are on the same (*cis*) or homologous (*trans*) chromosomes.

Recombination frequency is *not* a completely random event.

Specific regions within the chromosome have differences in the propensity to undergo recombination; the presence of *hotspots* and architectural features (e,g, histones) increase or decrease recombination frequencies.

Recombination frequency increases (not decreases) with *distance.*

Genes have different distances; with different distances, the recombination frequency changes.

37. C is correct.

There are two possible alleles for each of the three genes.

If the genes assort independently (not linked):

$$2^3 = 8 \text{ combinations exist}$$

38. A is correct.

Each affected person has an affected parent in the *autosomal dominant* inheritance pattern.

Autosomal dominant inheritance is a way a genetic trait can be passed from parent to child.

One parent's copy of a mutated (changed) gene can cause genetic conditions.

A child who has a parent with the mutated gene has a 50% chance of inheriting that mutated gene.

Men and women are *equally likely* to have these mutations.

Sons and daughters are *equally likely* to inherit them.

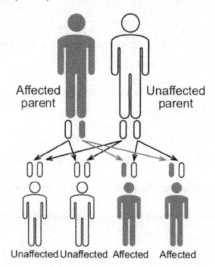

Autosomal dominant inheritance pattern with presence in each generation

39. C is correct.

Parents are Aa × Aa (carriers but not afflicted with the disease).

Progeny could be AA, Aa, Aa, or aa.

From the Punnett square, eliminate aa because this is the disease state.

The question asks the probability that she is heterozygous (Aa) but not homozygous (AA) = 2/3.

40. E is correct.

Anticipation is associated with an earlier onset of symptoms and increased disease severity in each generation.

Anticipation is observed in autosomal dominant diseases by *trinucleotide repeat expansions* (e.g., Huntington's disease, myotonic dystrophy) because increased-length triple repeats are unstable during cell division.

A: *codominance* is when a gene has more than one dominant allele. In the ABO blood group system, the I^A and I^B alleles are codominant.

Heterozygous individual for *two codominant alleles* expresses the phenotypes associated with both alleles.

Heterozygous individuals for the I^A and I^B alleles express the AB blood group phenotype, A- and B-type antigens are on the surface of red blood cells.

Codominance occurs at the locus for the beta-globin component of hemoglobin.

Three molecular phenotypes of Hb^A/Hb^A, Hb^A/Hb^S, and Hb^S/Hb^S are detectable by protein electrophoresis.

B: *penetrance* is the proportion of individuals carrying the variant of a gene (allele or genotype) and expressing the trait (phenotype).

In medical genetics, the penetrance of a disease-causing mutation is the proportion of individuals with the mutation who exhibit clinical symptoms.

For example, if a mutation in the gene responsible for an autosomal dominant disorder has 95% penetrance, 95% of those with the mutation develop the disease, while 5% do not.

D: *gain of function mutations* change the gene product to gain a new and abnormal function.

These mutations usually have dominant phenotypes and are expressed with a single allele.

41. B is correct.

Hardy-Weinberg equation:

$$p^2 + 2pq + q^2 = 1$$

where p equals gene frequency of dominant allele, and q equals gene frequency of recessive allele

Hence, in the population:

p^2 is the frequency of *homozygous dominants*

2pq is the frequency of *heterozygotes*

q^2 is the frequency of *homozygous recessives*

For a trait with two alleles, $p + q$ must equal 1 since the combined frequencies of the alleles = 100%.

If the frequency of the recessive allele for a trait is 0.6,

$$q = 0.6$$

Since

$$p + q = 1$$

$$p = 0.4$$

To calculate the frequency of individuals expressing the *dominant phenotype* (not the dominant genotype), determine the number of individuals *homozygous for the dominant trait* (p^2) and add the *number of heterozygotes* (2pq) exhibiting the dominant phenotype:

$$p^2 = (0.4) \times (0.4)$$

$$p^2 = 0.16$$

$$2pq = 2 \times (0.6) \times (0.4)$$

$$2pq = 0.48$$

So,

$$p^2 + 2pq = 0.16 + 0.48$$

$$p^2 + 2pq = 0.64$$

A: 0.48 = frequency of *heterozygous* individuals.

C: 0.16 = frequency of *homozygous dominant* individuals.

D: 0.36 = frequency of *homozygous recessive* individuals.

42. C is correct.

Maximum recombination frequency between two genes is 50%.

43. B is correct.

For a recessive trait to appear in a phenotype of an offspring (e.g., long hair), offspring inherit a recessive allele (Mendel called it *traits*) from each parent (i.e., two copies of the recessive gene).

Short-haired parents carry one copy (i.e., heterozygous) of the recessive long-haired allele (or *gene*).

Combined with the second copy from the other long-haired parent, it produced the long-haired offspring.

44. D is correct.

Meiosis in males produces four haploid (1N) unique cells genetically different from the parental cell.

45. D is correct.

Point mutations occur when a single nucleotide base (A, C, G, T) is substituted by another.

Silent mutation is a point mutation that

      1) occurs in a noncoding region or

      2) does not change the amino acid sequence due to the degeneracy of the genetic code.

Frameshift mutation is the insertion or deletion of some nucleotides. These mutations severely affect the coded protein since nucleotides are read as triplets.

Addition or loss of nucleotides (except in multiples of three) changes the reading frame of the mRNA and often gives rise to premature polypeptide termination (i.e., nonsense mutation).

Missense mutation results from the insertion of a single nucleotide that changes the amino acid sequence of the specified polypeptide.

46. E is correct.

Two reciprocal crossing-over events appear in progeny at an approximate ratio of 1:1.

47. C is correct.

EEBB × eebb produces offspring of single genotype EeBb, as determined by the Punnett square for the cross between a homozygous dominant by a homozygous recessive.

58. D is correct.

Mutations may cause *premature translation termination* (i.e., *nonsense* mutation) and nonfunctional protein.

49. E is correct.

	A	a
A	AA	Aa
a	Aa	aa

Afflicted children are AA, Aa or Aa (not aa) = 3 of 4 possibilities = ¾ or 75%.

50. D is correct.

Recombinant frequencies of linked genes map the relative locations of genes on a single chromosome.

Recombinant frequencies are determined by crossing individuals that differ in alleles for the genes in question and determining the genotypes of their progeny.

Recombinant frequencies equal frequencies of nonparent genotypes since these genotypes arise by crossover.

Mapping is based on the *probability* of a crossover between two points; the probability of crossover *increases* as the distance between the genes *increases*.

Farther away, genes have a *greater* recombinant frequency.

Probability that two genes are inherited together (i.e., linked) *decreases* as the distance between them on a chromosome *increases*.

One map unit = 1% recombination frequency, and recombinant frequencies are (roughly) additive.

However, if the genes are far apart, the recombination frequency reaches a *maximum of 50%,* at which point the genes are considered to be sorted independently.

There are four genes (D, E, F, and G), and the recombinant frequencies between each pair are given.

To construct the map, *start* with the allele pair with the *highest recombinant frequency*: between G and E (23%), which means that G and E are 23 map units apart and on the two ends.

Determine the intervening genes by finding the genes closest to the two endpoints.

G and D are 8 map units apart, closest to G. Thus, D must be next to G.

Genes on this chromosome must be G, D, F, and E by elimination.

EFDG is equally correct if the map started from the opposite direction, but this is not an answer choice.

To verify, D and E are 15 map units apart because the distance from G to D, which is 8, plus the distance from D to E, which is 15, is the distance from G to E, which equals 23.

G and F are 15 map units apart, while F and E are 8 units apart.

The numbers add, whereby the distance from G to E equals G to D + the distance from D to E.

The observed numbers may be off by one or two map units (not a mistake) because map distances are roughly additive (i.e., based on rounding for the probabilities).

Questions **51** through **57** are based on the following:

The pedigree illustrated by the schematic shows the inheritance of albinism, a homozygous recessive condition manifested in a total lack of pigment. Specify the genotypes using *A* and *a* to indicate dominant and recessive alleles.

Note: solids are albino individuals.

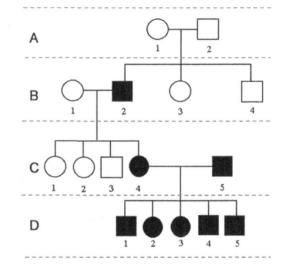

51. C is correct.

Individual A-1 in the pedigree is *Aa.*

52. C is correct.

Individual A-2 in the pedigree is *Aa.*

53. C is correct.

Individual B-1 in the pedigree is *Aa.*

54. B is correct.

Individual B-2 in the pedigree is *aa.*

55. C is correct.

Individual C-3 in the pedigree is *Aa.*

56. B is correct.

Individual C-4 in the pedigree is *aa.*

57. B is correct.

Individual D-4 in the pedigree is *aa.*

58. E is correct.

BBss × bbss produces gametes Bbss.

Then crossed:

Bbss × Bbss and produce the four gametes:

BBss, Bbss, bBss and bbss

Phenotypically,

¾ (BBss, Bbss, bBss) are black and spotted

¼ (bbss) is red and spotted

59. A is correct.

X-linked recessive inheritance is a mode of inheritance whereby a mutation in a gene on the X chromosome causes the phenotype to be expressed

1) *hemizygous males* with a single allele of the mutation because they have   one X chromosome and

2) *homozygous females* who are homozygous for the mutation (i.e., a copy of the gene mutation on each of two X chromosomes).

X-linked inheritance indicates that the gene is on the X chromosome.

Females have two X, while males have one X and one Y.

Carrier females have one allele and do not usually express the phenotype.

X-linked gene mutations are more common in males (i.e., a single allele of the X chromosome) than in females (i.e., two X chromosomes).

Gene appears to *alternate generations* because heterozygous phenotypically normal females transmit it.

Affected males transmit the gene to their daughters, carriers for the trait.

There is no father-to-son transmission because the sons inherit the father's Y chromosome.

Males carrying the mutant gene show the trait.

60. C is correct.

X-inactivation (i.e., lyonization) is when one of two X chromosomes in female mammals is inactivated.

Inactive X chromosome is silenced by transcriptional inactivity within heterochromatin (i.e., condensed DNA).

Females have two X chromosomes, and X-inactivation prevents them from having twice as many X chromosome gene products as males (XY) for dosage compensation of the X chromosome.

Which X chromosome becomes inactivated is random in humans.

Once an X chromosome is inactivated, it remains inactive throughout life and in descendants.

Calico and tortoiseshell-colored cats are phenotypic examples of *X-inactivation* because the alleles for black and orange fur coloration reside on the X chromosome.

For a patch of fur, inactivation of an X chromosome carries one gene resulting in the fur color of the allele for the active gene.

Calico cats are almost always female because the X chromosome determines the color of the cat, and female cats (like all female mammals) have two X chromosomes.

Male mammals have one X and one Y chromosome.

Y chromosome lacks color genes; there is no probability a male cat could have orange and non-orange.

One prominent exception is when, in rare cases, a male has XXY chromosomes (Klinefelter syndrome).

61. D is correct.

Autosomal dominance is typical Mendelian inheritance.

An individual needs a single copy of the mutant gene to exhibit the disease for *autosomal dominant* traits.

Autosomal dominance usually,

> equal numbers of males and females affected

> traits do not skip generations

> father-to-son transmission

62. E is correct.

Deletion of a portion of the Y chromosome containing the *testis-determining factor* results in some XY individuals being phenotypically female.

63. C is correct.

Inbreeding exposes recessive alleles by increasing *homozygosity* by one allele from each parent.

Closely related individuals are likely to carry alleles of *recessive genes* and have an increased probability of *passing recessive alleles* to their offspring.

64. D is correct.

Polyploidy refers to a numerical change in a complete set of chromosomes.

Most eukaryotic organisms are diploid (2N) with two sets of chromosomes – one set inherited from each parent.

Polyploid cells and organisms contain *more than two paired* (i.e., homologous) *sets of chromosomes*.

If crossing between two species is not possible because of differences in ploidy level, polyploids can be used as a bridge for gene transfer.

Additionally, polyploidy reduces fertility due to meiotic errors, allowing the cultivation of seedless varieties.

Polyploidy is in some organisms and is especially common in plants.

In addition, polyploidy occurs in some tissues of animals that are otherwise diploid (e.g., human muscle tissues).

65. C is correct.

Transgenesis introduces an exogenous gene (or *transgene*) into an organism to exhibit a new characteristic transmitted to its offspring.

Hybrid typically refers to the offspring of different species from interbreeding between two animals (or plants).

66. D is correct.

Plasmid is a small circular DNA molecule physically separate from chromosomal DNA within a cell and can replicate independently.

In nature, plasmids carry genes that may benefit the organism's survival (e.g., *antibiotic resistance in bacteria*) and can be transmitted among bacteria, even of another species.

Artificial plasmids are commonly used as vectors in molecular cloning to confer antibiotic resistance and drive the replication of recombinant DNA sequences within host organisms.

67. B is correct.

Transgenesis introduces an exogenous gene (a transgene) into an organism so that the organism develops a new characteristic and transmits it to offspring.

Hybrid in genetics has several meanings, the most common of which is the offspring resulting from the interbreeding between two animals or plants of different species.

68. B is correct.

DNA profiling (or *genetic fingerprinting*) is a laboratory technique to identify individuals by their DNA profiles.

DNA profiles are deoxyribose nucleotide bases (i.e., DNA used for identification.

Genetic fingerprinting (or DNA *profiling*) is used in paternity testing and criminal investigation and differs from complete genome sequencing (e.g., human genome project).

About 99.9% of human DNA sequences are the same.

DNA profiling distinguishes individuals with a high probability of certainty unless they are monozygotic (i.e., identical twins).

69. E is correct.

X-linked dominance is a mode of inheritance whereby a dominant gene is on the X chromosome.

X-linked dominant is less common than X-linked recessive.

For X-linked dominant inheritance, one allele is sufficient to cause the disorder when inherited from a parent who has the disorder.

X-linked dominant traits do not necessarily affect males more than females (unlike X-linked recessive traits).

An affected father has all affected daughters but no affected sons (unless the mother is also affected).

Notes for active learning

Notes for active learning

Essential Biology Self-Teaching Guides

Eukaryotic Cell & Cellular Metabolism

Molecular Biology & Genetics

Nervous & Endocrine Systems

Circulatory, Respiratory & Immune Systems

Digestive & Excretory Systems

Muscle, Skeletal & Integumentary Systems

Reproduction & Development

Microbiology

Plants & Photosynthesis

Evolution, Classification & Diversity

Ecology & Population Biology

Visit our Amazon store

Essential Chemistry Self-Teaching Guides

Electronic Structure & Periodic Table

Chemical Bonding

States of Matter & Phase Equilibria

Stoichiometry

Solution Chemistry

Chemical Kinetics & Equilibrium

Acids & Bases

Chemical Thermodynamics

Electrochemistry

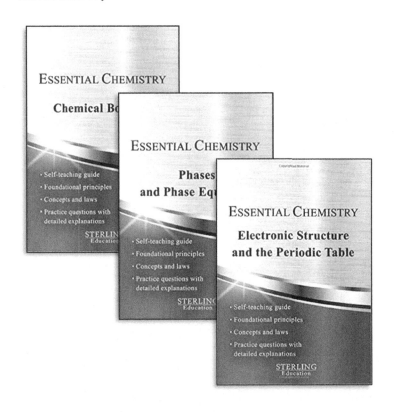

Essential Physics Self-Teaching Guides

Kinematics and Dynamics

Equilibrium and Momentum

Force, Motion, Gravitation

Work and Energy

Fluids and Solids

Waves and Periodic Motion

Light and Optics

Sound

Electrostatics and Electromagnetism

Electric Circuits

Heat and Thermodynamics

Atomic and Nuclear Structure

Visit our Amazon store

Everything You Always Wanted to Know About…

Chemistry

Physics

Cell and Molecular Biology

Organismal Biology

American History

American Law

American Government and Politics

Comparative Government and Politics

World History

European History

Psychology

Environmental Science

Human Geography

Made in the USA
Las Vegas, NV
30 November 2024

13001278R00138